THE ONEDIN LINE

The High Seas

In this, the third story of the Onedin family, it seems that James and Anne can at last begin to enjoy the fruits of their earlier struggles now that a public company has been launched for the construction of the first steamship of the Onedin Line. But in such a close-knit community as the shipping world of nineteenth-century Liverpool, success always has its enemies, and a crazy gamble offers James the chance to secure his position but the stakes are high.

*The Onedin Line story by Cyril Abraham
in the Ulverscroft Large Print Series:*

Book 1 *The Shipmaster*
Book 2 *The Iron Ships*
Book 3 *The High Seas*

————————◆————————

This Large Print Edition
is published by kind permission of
W. H. Allen & Co. Ltd.
London
and
The New American Library, Inc.
New York

CYRIL ABRAHAM

THE ONEDIN LINE
The High Seas

Complete and Unabridged

ULVERSCROFT
Leicester

First published in Great Britain in 1975 by
Allan Wingate (Publishers) Ltd.,
London

First Large Print Edition
published February 1979

British Library CIP Data

Abraham, Cyril
    The Onedin Line, the high seas.
    —Large print ed.
    (Ulverscroft large print series: general fiction).
    I. Title
    823'.9'1F   PR6051.B70/

    ISBN 0-7089-0266-9

Published by
F. A. Thorpe (Publishing) Ltd.
Anstey, Leicestershire
Printed in England

For
Ray and Chris

CHAPTER 1

WITH the white sea bubbling beneath her bows, the *Pampero* heeled and came round smartly into the wind. The port anchor leaped from the cathead and the plash of water as the flukes sought bottom set the seal on the voyage. The ship leaned back on the tautening cable, the yards rattled down and the white canvas was hauled in and furled. She'd made a fast run out to Alexandria and back with a precious cargo of Egyptian long staple. Now that the American civil war was entering its second bloody year, cotton was at a premium and ship-owners desperate for new markets. James had every reason to be satisfied. He looked along the snow-white decks, the gleaming varnishwork, the barefoot seamen cheerfully pattering about coiling and flaking lines.

'You'll do,' he said. 'You'll do very well, Mr Baines.' He'd allowed Baines to take the ship out and home in nominal command, an apprentice master learning his trade.

Baines beamed his pleasure. Praise from

Mr Onedin was a rare commodity, an especial dish to be savoured at leisure. He wiped his brow with a backward sweep of his arm.

'It's not that, Mr Onedin,' he returned. 'It's the figurin' that has me bothered.'

James understood. When it came to handling ships and men the giant had no equal, but once faced with a column of numbers he was as helpless as any Samson shorn of hair. It was a fact James could never comprehend. To him figures were instruments of precision, marshalling themselves like rows of orderly soldiers, never out of step. Two plus two formed four with an inescapable logic of its own.

Anne turned from her inspection of the Liverpool docks and a steam tug flying the tiger-striped Frazer flag already fussing out to meet them.

'Nonsense, Mr Baines,' she pronounced briskly. 'I have every confidence that you will pass with flying colours.' She smiled encouragement. 'It is simply a matter of concentration.'

James doubted it. Baines would never pass his master's examination though he

concentrated from now until dooms-
day.

Baines seemed to be of the same opinion,
for he scratched his poll ruefully. 'I can
count me beads with the best of 'em, but I
doubt I'll be allowed to take an abacus into
the examination room.'

James grunted, but remembering Anne's
patient teaching avoided Baines's eye. For
an hour every day the man had sat hunched
over that confounded child's plaything
laboriously calculating that which should
be immediately apparent to any thinking
being.

'Let us try a simple test,' Anne was
saying. 'Three times nine times eighteen, if
you please.'

James watched Baines screw his features
into a frown of ferocious concentration,
then expel a breath in a whoosh of sustained
effort. 'Four hundred and eighty-six?' he
answered hopefully.

James blinked, then nodded wonderingly. 'Four hundred and eighty-six, it is.'

Baines answered the unspoken query. 'I
just close me eyes and conjures up a picture
of that counting frame, push them little
beads around and add 'em up.' His moon

face wreathed into a smirk of false modesty. 'There's nothing to it once you got the hang of it.'

Anne adjusted her bonnet and tucked a renegade wisp of hair back into place. 'You see, James,' she said gently, 'Mr Baines really can take the abacus with him.'

She was laughing at him. He smiled back. She really was a most remarkable woman. 'I share Mrs Onedin's confidence, Mr Baines, and look forward to being the first to congratulate you.' He put as much sincerity as he could muster into his voice, but there was more to taking a master's certificate than a few parlour tricks.

The arrival of the tug put an end to further discussion. Paddles beating slowly, it came up on the *Pampero*'s lee, allowing the black smoke belching from its funnel to engulf an irate Callon ship swinging at anchor a few cable lengths away.

A bell dong-donged, the paddles stopped churning and as the tug bumped gently alongside they saw Albert standing on the starboard sponson. He wore trousers of a black and white dog-tooth check, blue high-buttoned frock-coat and yellow tie. He cheerfully waved a top hat of modish brown and his Mephistophelean features divided into a grin of welcome while the *Pampero* rolled uneasily in the latent wash of the tug. A seaman, hanging in the shrouds, stretched out a helping arm as thick as a hawser and the colour of teak. Albert jumped the yard of seething water, landed lightly on his feet and swept a bow in Anne's direction.

'Your servant, ma'am,' he said with grave formality and turned his bland gaze upon James. 'A profitable voyage, I trust?'

'Welcome aboard,' James replied with equal formality, wondering what possessed his dandified brother-in-law to make him tear himself away from his beloved drawing office. More than the pleasure of their company, he thought suspiciously.

'Elizabeth sends her regards,' Albert added almost as an afterthought.

The tug panted ahead and put out its tow line. A dozen hands shipped home the capstan bars and with lowered heads and straining backs commenced the long walk-and-heave around the trundlehead. The tug took the strain, the tramping feet stamped more quickly, the cable clattered in through the hawse pipe and above the wild skirling of the gulls and the deep thump of the tug's engines breathless voices chanted a rhythmic refrain:

'The boarding house masters is waiting
    ashore,
With the promise of booze and a fat greasy
    whore;
Telling the tale like Mother M'Cree.
Yer a fool me lad to follow the sea . . .'

Albert climbed the poop-deck ladder and smiled at James. 'You'll need every penny you can scrape together. I hear Callon has been busy snapping up shares.'

James sniffed. 'His money is as good as the next man's,' he said sourly.

'Better than yours,' Albert commented drily. 'There's more of it.'

James tugged at the lobe of his ear and took a pace or two along the deck while digesting the implications. He recollected lawyer Tapscott's advice: 'A joint-stock company being one in which shares are on offer to the public it behoves a prudent man to ensure that he has a majority holding, to wit, fifty-one per centum.' The Onedin Line Steamship Company had been capitalised with an issue of one hundred thousand shares. Fifty-one thousand pounds to find. James had shaken his head at the impossibility. The lawyer had inhaled a small mountain of snuff, pale watery eyes swimming behind thick-lensed spectacles. 'It is, in fact, entirely possible to keep effective control without indulging in the luxury of such gross expenditure. Shareholders being notoriously divisive in their opinions a forty per cent holding should be sufficient. Furthermore, you may, if you wish, call up but one half of your capital, the remainder remaining on call. That is to say each shareholder would pay ten shillings for a one-pound share and the balance on demand.' James had grasped the point immediately: anyone holding anything in excess of twenty-five thousand pounds' worth of stock would control the company. He had scraped together fifteen thousand pounds, thereby giving himself a thirty per cent interest. Albert had eighteen thousand shares, while Robert, after braying loud and long, had reluctantly invested a miserly five hundred pounds.

He walked to the shipside, gripped the rail and stared unseeingly at the moil of water flowing past the *Pampero*'s counter. Forty-nine thousand shares. A fair holding but three thousand short of absolute safety. This voyage should show a profit of around seven thousand pounds. He would instruct Tapscott to buy up every share in sight. Callon must be out for blood.

Albert joined him at the taffrail. 'He's been buying through nominees.' A frown of puzzlement etched parallel lines between his brows. 'What the devil is his game?'

'He's out to break us,' James told him flatly. 'If he once gains control his first action will be to call in the balance. It would cost you another nine thousand and you would never get your ship off the stocks. It would bankrupt me.'

A shadow of alarm drifted across Albert's face. 'Nine thousand at short notice? It's a great deal of money. I doubt if I could find it.' He seemed to think the admission deserving of explanation. 'Elizabeth has extravagant tastes.' He spoke petulantly and with an unaccustomed air of embarrassment.

'Callon can afford the luxury of losing,

we can't,' said James shortly, unimpressed with Albert's domestic problems. 'We must pick up every available share. What is Callon's present holding?'

Albert shrugged. 'It seems your clerk, Tupman, has been keeping his ear to the ground. Sharp fellow, that. Very sharp. Naturally he reported his findings to Robert.' He permitted himself a derisory grin. 'Robert came to me quite puffed up with pride, eager to put up an extra hundred. He appeared to be under the impression that any company which attracted Mr Callon's investments must of necessity be financially sound.'

James could well believe it. Robert had all the business acumen of a Hottentot. Nevertheless the notion amused him and he grinned back at Albert. 'Did he buy?'

'None to be had. Callon's buying has forced up the price. The remaining shareholders are sitting tight.'

This was serious. It indicated buying on a large scale. 'And you have no idea of the extent of Callon's holdings?'

Albert shook his head. 'Tupman is trying to find out.'

James nodded. 'I think I know how to

sharpen Mr Tupman's wits. In the meantime you concentrate on building the ship. I shall take care of the finances.'

The *Pampero*'s cable hung vertically. The tramp of feet quickened and the anchor stock rose to reach for the ship with dripping outstretched arms. The flukes kissed the water and the ship's head swung toward the five-storeyed warehouses and iron Doric columns of Albert Dock. The tug whistled hoarsely, the tempo of its paddles increased and the tow-rope strained to send multi-coloured rainbows dancing and shimmering across the gulf between steam and sail. The seamen's voices lifted to a triumphant howl:

'Roll, roll, roll, bullies, roll!
The Liverpool Judies has got us in tow!'

and the anchor cleared to swing lazily at the cathead.

Albert turned from the rail as Anne approached, long-hooped crinoline billowing against the pressure of the off-shore breeze. She hugged a black knitted woollen shawl about her narrow shoulders and her thin features were creased into a grin of welcome. Albert gallantly saluted the proffered hand, unfashionably brown from long exposure to the Mediterranean sun and the burning winds of the sea.

'You are the picture of health, Anne,' he told her warmly, wondering why on earth the woman, commonsensical in most matters, should be so lacking in sensibility as to subject both face and hands to the deleterious effects of sunlight, notoriously fickle to a lady's complexion. At any society gathering she would stand out like a gypsy. He sighed, aware that she cared not a fig for popular accord, and embarked upon his second piece of news.

'You could not have arrived at a more opportune moment.' He coughed delicately. 'For the wedding, you know.'

They stared at him blankly.

Albert touched his moustache, savouring the moment. 'Fogarty and Emma Callon. Chap's a damned fortune-hunter, of course. Always knew there was something unprincipled about the feller. Wormed his way into Callon's confidence and snapped up the daughter.'

Anne thought she understood Albert's bitterness. 'I am sure you misread Mr

Fogarty's character; he has always impressed me as a young man of the utmost probity.'

Albert's nose lifted in a well-bred air of dissent and his fingers drummed a tattoo upon the roof of his hat as he consigned Daniel Fogarty to the limbo of obscurity.

'The man has no family,' he pronounced coldly.

An armada of clouds massed like galleons to bombard the river with bolts of sunlight. The tug ploughed twin furrows of white wake, its engines banging and clattering an affront to their hearing; the rancid stench of hot grease and oil invaded their nostrils to replace the long-familiar pungency of tar and hemp. Acrid black smoke, swirling and eddying in the wind, swept across the *Pampero*'s decks, driving them to seek shelter below.

Baines, left in charge, surveyed his world with a proprietorial air.

The river was busy with shipping. A line of timber ships from Canada and the Baltic wallowed in line, queueing for berths in the new Canada Dock. To the south men worked like busy ants, quarrying red sandstone as they carved out the basin of the long-delayed Herculaneum dock. Baines counted twenty-one docks, all packed with ships: Indiamen were discharging in Albert; George's was full of fruit schooners; brigs and snows of continental traders lay side by side in King's and Queen's; gouts of steam boiled up from the tall funnels of steamships with smoke-grimed sails as they sounded eerie warnings to the piled canvas of Australian wool clippers beating upriver. Across the river, on the Birkenhead side, the Great Float was open to shipping and a great press of masts, spars and sails towered above green fields and clusters of houses. The furnace-roar of Laird's iron foundry, competing with the ring of hammers from his shipyards, stammered their challenge to white-winged ships laden with the stores of the earth.

Ferry boats paddled across the water and at the Pier Head Landing Stage a ringing of bells and toot-tooting of whistles announced the imminent departures of the Isle of Man steam packet ships. Decks a turmoil of shouting and waving passengers, paddles beating the muddy waters of the Mersey into a froth of white foam, the two ships moved out to take up station in midstream.

Baines watched with interest as the massive iron-plated *Mona's Queen* began to surge ahead of her rival, the diminutive *Manx Fairy*. The smaller ship had the more graceful lines. A delicate toy, painted blue and gold with the arms of Man emblazoned upon her paddle boxes. She also had a deceptive turn of speed, coupled with an enormous appetite for coal. White-painted paddles flailing the water, the tiny craft drove into arrowheads of surf thrown aside by the larger vessel's clipper bows.

He shook his head at the folly of it all. The current mania for speed drove ship to challenge ship across the oceans of the world. Sailers held on to canvas until the violence of the wind plunged them beneath the wild sea; steamers shook themselves to pieces or else exploded their boilers in a frenzied determination to prove their superiority over sail. The sailing-ship men jeered and hung out tow-ropes, taunting the labouring steamboats with mocking cries of 'Yer kettle's gone off the boil' and 'Put another lump on the fire'. But lately the good humour seemed to have turned sour and there was a sense of anger in the air. On the waterfronts there would be sporadic outbursts of fighting between the two factions. The world was changing, and not for the better, in Baines's opinion.

CHAPTER 2

IT was the last white-stocking day of the voyage and the seamen's wives had gathered in their finery of black shawls, high-buttoned boots and traditional white stockings—well known to be the hallmark of a lady of quality. They hung around Robert's shop, chirruping and quarrelling like a flock of multi-coloured starlings while the queue of seamen snaking from the 'Onedin Line Shipping Office' above wagged its tail in the street outside.

James sat at the desk, the ship's Articles of Agreement open in front of him. As each man shuffled forward to sign his name or, more often than not, make his mark, James droned out the amount due. It had been a short voyage of but ninety-eight days, most of which had been spent in port discharging and loading. At £2–10–0 a month, one month's blood-money in advance to the crimping-house master who supplied the crew, and a monthly allotment to their wives, the return seemed scant reward for three months' hard labour.

'Next,' said James, and Kees the Dutchman stepped forward to sheepishly knuckle his forehead, sign his indecipherable name with a flourish and hold out a massive fur-backed paw. James's clerk, Tupman, meticulously counted out the sum of £5-3-4 from which had been deducted a fine of five shillings for drunk and disorderly behaviour plus a further five shillings for carelessly losing an oaken bucket. Kees obviously bore no grudge for his loss, for he grinned hugely, collected his discharge paper, pocketed his pay, bade James a cheerful 'T'ankee, Cap'n,' and shouldered his way out to head for the delights of Fiddler's Green, the seaman's Elysium of crimps, pimps and prostitutes. Kees no doubt would wake up one morning aboard some skysail-yarder bound round the Horn. James glanced down at the Articles: the Dutchman had left no allotment nor named a next-of-kin; evidently he was one of that restless band of nomads who drifted like flotsam across the face of the sea until some far-away beach claimed their bones.

James's gaze wandered over the office. Blackened oak rafters supported the pitch of the roof to show the scaly undersides of slates rattling drily in the wind. Dust motes danced and whirled in shafts of pale sunlight falling from oblique skylights; a cascade of gold poured upon a corner of the long narrow clerks' desk to spill to the bare floor in a shimmering yellow pool. Oven-hot in summer, ice-cold in winter, the room had little to recommend it beyond convenience and cheapness.

Tupman's pen scratched busily. The last seaman collected his pay. Sunlight wavered like a silken banner; cartwheels rumbled on the cobbles outside; a voice rose in a shout of laughter and a blackbird whistling contentedly to itself beneath the eaves took sudden flight with a shriek of alarm.

James yawned and stretched and waited patiently for Tupman to balance the accounts. He watched the clerk's pen racing up the columns of figures with barely a pause of hesitation. Tiny beads of perspiration glistened on the waxed face while the thin lips moved in a silent incantation of addition and subtraction. He entered the totals, ruled a neat line and passed the ledger across for James's inspection. James nodded approval and closed the book.

'How much do we pay you, Mr Tupman?'

It was a rhetorical question to which both knew the answer. Tupman licked his lips and prayed that Mr James was not about to suggest a cut in wages. With potatoes at a penny a pound, butcher's meat at ninepence, and a quartern loaf costing tenpence he did not see how he could possibily subsist on anything less than his present emolument.

'Twelve shillings, sir,' he answered, and felt a clamminess at the nape of his neck.

James scooped the remaining coins into the palm of his hand and jingled them thoughtfully. Gold and silver gleamed in the soft half-light.

'We'll make it fifteen shillings, Mr Tupman,' he stated abruptly. 'As of Monday.'

Tupman could not believe his good fortune and began to stammer a paean of gratitude. James cut him short with a wave of his hand.

'The labourer,' he said sententiously, ' is worthy of his hire,' and had the grace to reflect that if such were the case then the clerk had been grossly underpaid even by the standards of a notoriously over-exploited profession. 'I wonder,' he added, striking while the iron was hot, 'if you could carry out a small commission for me?'

Tupman bobbed his head feverishly, only too anxious to prove his worth. Any task, however menial—Mr James had only to command.

Mr James did. 'A confidential inquiry,' he said. 'I should like to know—discreetly—the precise extent of Mr Callon's holdings in my company, and the names of his nominees. Do you think you could manage that?'

Tupman paused to reflect. His clerk's brain selected and rejected from lists of acquaintances and came to the reluctant conclusion that only one man filled the bill.

'Drummond,' he said. 'I believe he might be open to . . .' He hesitated delicately. 'Suggestion.'

'Bribery,' said James, and counted out ten half-sovereigns. He pushed them across to Tupman. 'Bait. A little at a time, Mr Tupman. Avarice feeds upon expectation.'

'I understand, sir.' Tupman carefully deposited the money in his purse, snapped it shut and placed it within the safety of his fob pocket. Drummond! He remembered the wretch only too vividly. The ferret face and air of rat-like cunning; servile to his employers, bombastic to those he considered his inferiors; Callon's creature who had once led him into the temptation and pitfall of drink in furtherance of perfidy. Yes, Drummond should fill the bill very nicely, very nicely indeed.

Drummond, head bent low over his copywork, risked raising a furtive eye in the direction of Mr Agnew as that desiccated tyrant embarked upon the first stage of his evening ritual. First he would close the company register followed by the general ledger, the personal ledger, the private ledger and finally the cash book. These were then gathered in to a benedictory pile to sit at the chief clerk's right hand while the lesser acolytes, if they knew what was good for them, kept their heads bowed in silent worship. For heaven help any scribbler unfortunate enough to show signs of relaxation during these last few minutes.

That unhappy wretch would not only receive an acidulated inquiry as to whether he considered his labours sufficient unto the day but also be invited to remain behind for a further half-hour that he may fully appreciate the value of the adage that time is a commodity which once spent may never be recovered. Drummond himself had suffered the ignominy too often in the past to be caught out now, so he applied himself with even greater diligence to his work of transcribing invoices.

From the superior height of the raised dais Agnew surveyed his little kingdom. The silence was broken only by the scratching of pens and the whispering expiration of breath. He detached his heavy silver hunter from its chain, snapped open the case and laid it face upward upon the desk.

Drummond was convinced that the swine did it a-purpose in the knowledge that sooner or later the maddeningly rapid tickerty-tick, tickerty-tick would drive him out of his mind. He enscribed the particulars slowly in characterless rounded copperplate, his ears pricked in anticipation of Agnew's next move. It wasn't long in coming: the chair creaked as the chief clerk levered himself to his feet preparatory to making his final rounds. Stoop-shouldered, hands clasped behind his back, he paced slowly along the line of clerks, pausing occasionally to inspect calligraphy and legibility; invariably he tut-tutted tetchily at the carrot-headed Arnold's backward-sloping hand before breathing his infernal foetid breath down Drummond's neck. No inspection could pass without comment and tonight's was no exception.

'Your handwriting is atrocious, Drummond, atrocious,' said the hated voice and moved on.

Drummond sighed with relief as the sour-visaged old buzzard returned to his eyrie. One day he promised himself, one day he would repay that doddering old goat a thousandfold.

The doddering old goat subjected the scribblers to one final basilisk stare, checked that the second hand of the watch agreed with the minute hand that it was indeed precisely six o'clock, pursed his lips and pronounced his evening dictum:

'Very well, gentlemen, you may complete your work.'

Drummond knew better than to rush matters. He added a forbidden curlicue to the tail of a 'g', crossed a 't' and dotted an 'i', sharpened the quill pens ready for the morning and wiped the iron nibs of the stick pens on a felt pad. Only then did he impale the original invoice on to a spiked file and stack the copies beneath a lead paper-weight. His fellow clerks were shuffling to their feet, pushing back their stools. He trooped out with the rest, adding his voice to the polite chorus of 'Good-night, Mr Agnew', and silently wished the old pinchfist boiled in oil. Then he was free and scampering down the stairs with fourpence in his pocket and a thirst that would shame the devil.

Callon's office fronted on the Goree. St George's dock lay opposite, packed with shipping. A score of carts stood with empty shafts beneath warehouse hoists while penny-ostlers led massive shire horses to stone drinking troughs and their masters wet their whistles in the vaults beneath. Ship-brokers' offices nudged arms with emigrant agents and provision merchants with commission agents. Wine and spirit vaults leaned tipsily against gin shops and ale houses. The iron-shod wheels of whitechapels and broughams ground over the cobbles while teams of horses, panting and straining against their harness, hauled wagon-loads of grain to the waiting mills. Hoarse-voiced street vendors bawled their wares, messenger boys scampered through wheeling groups of nut-brown seamen and bright-plumed prostitutes. Staid, top-hatted business men in tightly buttoned frock-coats steadfastly ignored the bawdy life eddying and swirling about them.

Drummond emerged from the stifling confinement of the office into slanting sunlight and a fresh river breeze that, sporting across the square, bowled before it an errant top hat and a swarm of screeching urchins. He fingered the four pennies nestling in his pocket and decided to expend one on a hot pie. That should leave sufficient tin for a penn'orth of ale and a tuppenny gin. With luck he might find a convivial companion willing to stand treat.

The piestall was one of a row of temporary shacks constructed of matchboarding, tar paper and old tarpaulins huddled beneath the Goree arches. Coffee, cocoa and sherbet stalls rubbed shoulders with pea-soup and pig's-trotter vendors, while the sellers of kidney puddings and hot green peas vied for trade with hot-potato men and pork-pie men. All were doing a roaring business. The muffin-man's lad swung his bell deafeningly, drowning the chant of the fried-fish seller crying his wares in a monotonous dirge of 'Fried fish, a penny a piece. Fried fish a penny a piece.'

Drummond selected a mutton-and-potato-pie man whose delicacies he had sampled before. He shouldered his way through to the counter and was in the act of making his purchase when behind him a once-familiar voice said, 'Hold on, Drummond old man. My treat.'

He turned his head in disbelief to find the whey-face features of that smarmy-voiced, hymn-singing, back-scratcher Tupman smirking at him. Screwing his own features into a grimace of welcome, and on the principle of never looking a gift horse—however ill-favoured—in the mouth, he acknowledged acceptance of the offer with the hauteur of one long accustomed to such small supplications for his patronage.

'Hullo, Tupman. Civil of you. Deuced civil,' he responded condescendingly and quickly returned his penny to his pocket.

Tupman led the way and they carried their pies to a nearby Cocoa Rooms, a bare inhospitable-looking eating house of brown paint and marble-topped tables. Steam from large copper urns condensed in little droplets and clouded the windows so that passers-by seemed to move through a fog. Temperance Society posters clung damply to the walls exhorting all to Beware of the Demon Drink and recommending the nutritious benefits of cocoa. A few artisans and seedy-looking clerks in threadbare suits occupied a scattering of tables. A more dreary collection of dismal crows Drummond could not imagine. But a free pie and cup of cocoa would put a lining on his stomach and the penny saved he could now afford the luxury of two tuppenny gins. He wondered if the seemingly affluent Tupman could be persuaded to advance a small loan? Sixpence, or perhaps a shilling? A shilling, he decided as Tupman returned from the counter carrying two large steaming mugs of cocoa, a shilling at least. He bit into his pie and flourished a handkerchief to dab away a trickle of gravy running down his chin.

'Capital pie,' he pronounced with the air of a connoisseur. 'Capital. Sorry I can't return the favour, old man, but'—he uttered a short barking laugh—'the fact is I'm a little short of the ready. Until the end of the week, that is.' He broke off, his eyes widening as Tupman produced a newly minted gold half-sovereign from his pocket and casually spun it upon the table.

'Heard anything of Blenkinsop?' Tupman asked casually.

Drummond looked suspiciously at his fellow clerk, but the young-old face betrayed nothing but mild interest.

'I hope, old man,' he said hastily, 'you don't imagine I had anything to do with that business?'

Tupman munched and swallowed a mouthful of pie.

'What business would that be, old man?' he asked innocently.

Drummond wriggled uncomfortably and wondered how on earth such a duffer had managed to escape. Blenkinsop was aboard a Yankee windbag bound for Valparaiso and this simple-minded lackwit should be with him. Lord, but Callon has been in quite a bate and Agnew had given him the worst roasting of his life on learning of Tupman's return. He had expected instant dismissal, but the storm had blown over, as storms do; and here was the fellow as large as life standing pie and cocoa as though the whole confounded business had never happened.

He watched Tupman tossing the gold coin idly in his hand.

'Well—you know,' he said half-apologetically. 'The last time we met. Had a little tiddly together in the Lazarette, remember?'

'In celebration of Blenkinsop's bet-rothal, as I recollect,' Tupman responded gravely, adding by way of good measure, 'I imagine the young lady to be quite inconsolable?'

'Oh, cut up. Quite cut up. Yes, indeed,' Drummond mumbled quickly, and took refuge in a draught of thick sweetened cocoa. Good Lord, he thought, the fool must still believe that story.

'I'm afraid I can't offer anything stronger

than cocoa,' Tupman was saying. 'But I'm Temperance now, you see.'

'Ah,' said Drummond, cursing his luck. 'Very wise, old man. Very wise. Wish I could give the stuff up.' He eyed the gold coin pointedly. 'Small wonder publicans grow fat and rich.'

Tupman smiled, laid the coin on the table top, then drew another from his pocket. He placed it beside its fellow and began to circle the coin enticingly, like a golden moon circling a golden sun.

'Mr Onedin is a generous master. Generous to a fault.' He saw the cupidity in the tiny, almost lashless, rat-eyes opposite. 'Pays well for services rendered. This is just a little on account.'

'Oh?' Drummond licked his lips.

'A simple enough commission for persons in our line of business, Mr Drummond.' Tupman laid a knowing finger alongside his nose. 'For who knows more about a man's affairs than his clerk, eh? I daresay you could tell a story or two if you had a mind to it?'

'True, Mr Tupman, very true. They see us as nothing but quill-pushers, think we've no souls except of a Sunday, no

30

hearts save as vessels for pumping, no feelings beyond lumps of wood. It's scribble, scribble, scribble the live-long day with cheap pens and wore-out quills and inks that clog and splatter; but for all that I keep my ears open and my counsel to myself. I tell you, Mr Tupman, there's little passes in that office that escapes my attention.'

'As I remember you were always sharp of eye and sharp of wits, Mr Drummond.' Tupman leaned forward and lowered his voice to a confidential whisper. 'In fact, old man, there is a small matter which I am sure I could trust to your discretion.' The gold coin rang its promise upon the table top.

'If I can obligate you in any fashion, Mr Tupman, you have but to say the word.' Drummond closed a conspiratorial eye and by way of emphasis sucked at a piece of meat lodged between his teeth.

'It has come to our notice,' said Tupman with the air of a man habitually privy to his employer's confidences, 'that Mr Callon has been buying into Onedin Line Steamships. You would find us grateful for any information you might acquire in that particular during the course of your duties. In essence,' the half-sovereign moved temptingly forward, 'in essence the names and addresses of his nominees.'

Drummond drew in a breath. 'Difficult, Mr Tupman. Very difficult. Such information does not pass through the office, as well you know.'

Tupman shrugged, drained his cocoa and wiped his lips with an air of finality.

'It will be recorded in either the private register or private memorandum. However, if you find the commission over-burdensome do not hesitate to withdraw; I shall be put to no more than the minor inconvenience of combing through our share register.' Not so much inconvenient, he thought, as nigh impossible.

Drummond gnawed at a wisp of moustache hanging beneath a long inquisitive nose. He washed his hands together in an anguish of frustrated expectancy as the promise of reward seemed to dwindle. The sight of Tupman about to pocket the coins sharpened his wits. The memorandum book would be in Callon's private office. All that was required was to find a pretext for staying behind with Agnew out of the way. He held out a restraining hand.

'I'll do it, Mr T,' he declared firmly. 'And I trust you will bring this little service to Mr Onedin's notice?'

The piece of gold slid across the table. Drummond scooped it into the palm of his hand and whisked it away into his waistcoat pocket. He quite missed the irony in Tupman's voice.

'I assure you, Mr D,' he pronounced gravely, 'that Mr Onedin will be the first to know of your loyalty, and I have no doubt that you will be suitably rewarded.' He opened his purse and slid the remaining half-sovereign into its open mouth, but not before Drummond had caught a tantalising glimpse of the gleam of yet more bright yellow metal nestling inside.

Tupman closed and pocketed the purse, bade an affable good evening, and took his leave satisfied that Mr James would shortly acquire the information he needed.

CHAPTER 3

AN echoing din rose like the clamour of the damned from an inferno of heat and smoke. Far below a high-girdered gallery grinning red mouths belched fire and flame and licked the floor with white-hot tongues. Half-naked black-faced demons carried ladles of fire amid cascades of burning gold. Others slaved to feed the roaring hunger of a row of round-bellied idols. Iron rang against iron. A hammer-nosed monster gouted steam and shook the earth with ponderous blows. Cinders rose like fireflies from the scorching breath of a giant forge.

Heat beat up at them in sulphurous waves, making eyes smart and throats burn. Anne imagined that Pandemonium, the abode of the devils, could be no worse, and turned her head to observe her companions. Albert, bathed in the ruddy glow of the furnaces, looked more Mephistoph-elean than ever. He was leaning forward watching every movement with total concentration. James stood in brooding meditation, his face closed in thought. Elizabeth was fanning her face with a wisp of cambric. Her mouth opened and closed like a stranded fish and she rolled her eyes toward Anne in wry supplication.

They had been invited to attend the ceremony of casting the keel, but anything less ceremonious Anne could not imagine, although she understood that Albert had donated two barrels of ale for the gnome-like figures labouring below, and they themselves were shortly to take a glass of iced champagne with the foundry master, a man of leathered features puckered with veins and a voice of brass who was at that moment directing operations from the foundry floor.

Albert touched James's shoulder and pointed. Speech in that deafening clamour was out of the question.

A furnace was being tapped, and even as they looked workmen who had been prodding and prising with long iron bars sprang back as a light of searing incandescence suddenly appeared at the bottom of the oven. Then with a roar a mass of molten metal gushed out to be channelled to the waiting mould. At first it

35

poured in thick whiteness, then dark veins and leprous pustules began to appear while men ran beside it hacking and slicing at the cherry-red coating of slag. Others swung hammers beating it into shape. Anne's eyes hurt and ached and she marvelled that men could survive, much less work under such conditions. Then to her great relief Albert clapped James upon the shoulder and guided them away through a heavy door and out upon a wrought-iron balcony that ran beneath an arched buttress and clung to the wall like a Moorish arabesque.

The air was cool and sweet and the great bowl of the sky hung with clouds. They made their way down a diamond-patterned stairway and crossed a cobbled courtyard with the din of hammers still ringing in their ears. At the office they took champagne and exchanged civilities with Mr Palfrey, the foundry master, whose bright red hair was turning ashen so that his head seemed to have been scorched by fire. The only remark worthy of note was when James asked Albert how long it would take from the casting of the keel to launching. Nine months, Albert had told him, and Anne had smiled and decided to hug her secret to herself a little longer. Then they were in their carriage and bowling along at a smart clip.

'What now?' asked Elizabeth, as always ever-reluctant to call upon the day to end.

'We celebrate,' said Albert, and the carriage threaded its way through a network of streets and Elizabeth's heart stormed into her throat when the coachman drew on the reins and the horses came to a steaming halt beside a once-familiar, never-to-be-forgotten restaurant.

The same restaurateur of forked beard and cannonball head greeted them at the doorway as had greeted herself and Daniel on that night of bewitchment so long, long ago. She hung her head and blushed furiously, convinced that she would be instantly unmasked, an indignity suffered by Carrie Carstairs in *Mistaken Identity*. Miss Carstairs had succumbed to a fit of the swoons and lost the use of her wits to the end of her days.

Elizabeth kept her wits about her by indulging in a torrent of inconsequential chatter as they were escorted to their table by a flurry of waiters, only stopping to draw breath as the hotelier handed round the selfsame enormous menu cards and she was satisfied that the politely opaque eyes held not the slightest hint of recognition. While Albert, the linguist of the party, translated for them, she stole a glance at the raftered ceiling and wondered if the private room was still in use as a place of assignation. Memory stole like a summer sun through mists of forgetfulness and once again she saw the silk-hung mirrors, the low gas jets popping within pink glass bowls and yellow tongues of flame thrusting up the chimney to paint the room with wild dancing shadows. Daniel. Dear Daniel . . . She tore her mind away from the snare of the dream with the realisation that dear Daniel would shortly be marrying that odious Emma Callon. What he could possibly find attractive in such an insipid creature she could not imagine, and came out of her reverie to hear Albert recommending jugged hare à la St Hubert. She agreed indifferently, discovering that she had of a moment lost her appetite. Then, seeing a tiny frown of concern upon dear Albert's brow, was suddenly contrite. She reached out, smiled and touched his hand.

'I am sure it will be delicious,' she said,

adding by way of tempting the devil, 'with a bottle of champagne to wash it down.'

'Two bottles of the Widow,' Albert instructed Baldhead, and gallantly raised her hand to his lips.

James ate stolidly through the meal with his usual lack of appreciation. He swallowed champagne as though it were water and chewed at jugged hare and truffles as though chomping his way through a platter of ship's victuals.

Anne toyed with her food, barely touched her wine and confined her conversation to commonplaces, as though her thoughts were revolving about some inner problem the complexity of which was imperfectly understood.

Albert aimed his conversation directly at James, firing fusillades of facts and figures with the prodigality of a man with ammunition to spare, until even he realised that he was but throwing stones into an ever-widening pool of silence.

For some unaccountable reason an air of gloom and despondency seemed to have settled over the meal and each began secretly to wish that the affair might come to an end that they may return to their own private worlds. By common consent they forwent coffee. Albert settled the bill and they trooped to the door where Baldhead bowed them out.

'Thank you, Henri,' Albert told the man politely. 'An excellent meal.'

The cannonball head dipped in response.

'*Toujours à votre service, M'sieu Freesair. Mesdames. M'sieu.*'

The carriage was waiting; the horses dozing between the shafts, the coachman occupying his time in plaiting a new whip and carrying on a rancorous argument with a group of idlers on the merits and demerits of slavery.

It seemed, James thought sourly, handing Anne into the carriage, one of those never-ending topics of discussion in which ignorance was never a bar to opinion.

By the time they reached the house and thanked Albert for his hospitality the lamplighters were making their rounds and the yellow glow of gas lanterns cut swathes of light through the darkness. The coachman sat wrapped in silence while the horses arched their necks and blew twin clouds of steam into the night. A rosy moon hung over the house tops like a Chinese lantern to throw castellated shadows across the square.

Then they were home, and James immediately stretched out in his favourite chair, feet toward the cheerfully blazing fire, while Ruby, the parlourmaid, flitted about the room lighting the gas lamps. Anne divested herself of cloak and bonnet and waited until Ruby had added a couple more knobs of coal to the grate, bobbed a respectful curtsey and left, before imparting her news.

'James—' she began, tentatively. 'James—?'

A lump of glowing coal tumbled into the fire to send tongues of flame flickering and dancing. Shifting planes of light and shade passed across his features. He was asleep. She smiled to herself. No matter. Tomorrow would do. Her news would keep.

Elizabeth adjusted the side curtain of the tester before wriggling sensuously into the warm embrace of the goose-feathered mattress. Albert dozed by her side, his tasselled nightcap at a rakish angle. Dear Albert. She had so much to be grateful for.

He had been more than usually solicitous of late and at last it seemed that those horrid dark suspicions had finally been laid to rest. Why, he now quite doted on their son and was positively overjoyed when the child raised chubby arms and quite clearly enunciated 'Papa', and although William's mop of hair was distinctly dark of colouring nothing whatsoever could be deduced from the features, which were of a pale milk-and-honey softness, not in the least like Daniel's swart visage. Furthermore, Daniel habitually wore a full beard which effectively concealed his true appearance. In fact she had often tried to imagine him clean-shaven, but had never succeeded in conjuring up anything other than plain ordinary nondescript features. She banished Daniel's spectre back to the limbo from which it had emerged unbidden and settled herself into mulling over the events of the day. She decided that she rather liked dining in the French fashion and idly wondered how Albert had learned of the place. She was drifting off to sleep, already beginning to purr in blissful contentment, when like a falling star a thought dropped into her consciousness, flared and died.

'Albert—?'

'Mm?'

'That restaurant. However did you find such a lovely place?'

Albert mumbled drowsily into the pillow.

'Recommended by a chap at the club. G'night.'

'Good night, dear heart,' she said, satisfied. Then suddenly came awake with the recollection of Albert addressing the hotelier by first name and the man replying in that funny French accent. Missy Freezer, he'd said, and she knew with absolute certainty that the two were on terms of familiarity.

She lay awake for a long time watching the moon trace patterns of silver upon the ceiling while her brain picked and pecked at the problem until she finally fell into a troubled sleep to dream of a faceless Daniel pursued by a gloating Emma while she ran through a forest of fire with William clutched in her arms and Albert, seated upon Satan's throne of molten iron, brooded over all.

CHAPTER 4

JAMES wandered aimlessly about the docks lost in thought. Callon's sudden raid upon the market had blown his future plans to pieces. His mind seemed to run in circles, whirling like a frozen wind about a solitary pole. Money. Callon had the financial resources to outbid him at every call. Callon had bided his time and then struck at the most vulnerable point: the company shares. Callon had the game won. James cursed himself for the folly of going public. He'd been too impetuous, allowed himself to be carried away on a tide of enthusiasm. He should have waited, built a fleet of sail, then and only then ploughed the profits into steam. He shook his head, knowing in his heart that the decision had been correct. The time was now, not tomorrow. Tomorrow smacked of brother Robert's counsel.

He paused on the sea wall. To his right lay the docks packed with shipping, to his left the busy river. The wind blew sharp and clean with the taste of salt. Gulls floated overhead calling high-pitched lamentations. In King's dock he noticed ranks of broad-beamed shallow-draught Mississippi cotton droghers, laid up no doubt on account of that damned war. Nor were they alone. Out in the river lay other ships, moored end to end. Now would be the time to buy while prices were at rock bottom. A second *Pampero*. He'd paid off Braganza's share and seven thousand pounds were burning a hole in his pocket. One of the ships caught his interest. He remembered her name, the *Andromeda*, from among the 'For Sale' notices in that morning's *Shipping Gazette*, and even from this distance he could see she was distinguished by the figurehead of a distraught-looking lady chained beneath the bowsprit. He moved on a pace or two and almost tripped over a line attached to a ringbolt. Looking down, he saw a grizzled roly-poly in seaman's guernsey and duck trousers asleep on the bottom boards of a wherry. A length of line attached to the big toe of one dirty bare foot trailed over the side to a crude float bobbing on the lapping waves. It was high tide and slack water. On impulse James clambered down the footholds, white with bird droppings and bearded with weed, cut into the granite face of the seawall. The man sat up, rubbed sleep from his eyes, philosophically hauled in the empty line, and squinted a gap-toothed inquiry.

'Put me aboard the *Andromeda*,' James commanded, and settled himself in the sternsheets.

The ferryman rowed with professional ease and the shallow wherry skimmed across the flat oily calm of the river. James studied the *Andromeda*'s lines with care. A cable length away he ordered the man to row slowly around the ship.

She was sheathed in iron and rust stains showed through once-white paint. Her bows were bluff and the tumblehome markedly pronounced. Designed for bulk cargo and slow passages, he decided. She was a barquentine with three stubby masts and heavy gear. A brute of a ship and a regular workhouse for the crew, but she'd take a deal of knocking about. A heavy-weather ship standing high out of the water. Even with a gutful of cargo there would be too much windage for comfort. She'd sail like a crab and a lee shore would be a nightmare to her master, but with coal out and grain home she could turn a decent profit. He noticed approvingly that a bull rope was attached to the bowsprit and led down to the mooring buoy, this preventing the stem from chafing against the buoy at times of slack water. The stern was rounded and the massive rudder, dipping into the sea with every rise and fall of the swell, was encrusted with weed and barnacles. The bottom no doubt would be in like condition, thereby reducing her way by at least two knots, but a couple of days in dry dock would cure that problem.

James hailed the deck and as the wherry bumped alongside a Jacob's ladder was inexpertly lowered over the side. James tested it carefully before trusting his weight to the slatted rungs, then went up hand over hand with the ease of long practice. He took a purchase on the mainmast backstay and swung down to the deck to be greeted by a stoop-shouldered dispirited-looking man of characterless features, dank hair plastered across a balding head and unevenly trimmed muttonchop whiskers. The man introduced himself as a Mr Potter, clerk to the agent, and, washing his hands in the waters of anxiety, pronounced that his instructions were to offer every possible assistance and facility, and that he, himself, would be more than honoured if the gentleman would favour him with his confidence.

'In short,' said James, 'I can poke and pry as much as I choose,' and brusquely dismissed the imbecile before the fellow launched into a long-prepared, oft-rehearsed speech extolling the virtues and flawless performances of this wonder among ships. Then he methodically tramped around the decks, testing, checking, examining every nook and cranny. Even so, he found his inspection somewhat half-hearted, his brain still engaged in an invisible tug-of-war.

At length he stood upon the high poop deck and surveyed the length of the ship. Stocky and sound of timber, she should suit very well the purpose for which she was built. And he had little doubt that she could be had cheaply. The temptation was strong. A ship such as the *Andromeda* could be an excellent investment. The equation was simple enough. The more ships, the greater the profits. Buy the ship and somehow stave off Callon until he'd cleared sufficient profit to bid for the remaining shares. Something gnawed at the back of his mind and out of habit he slowly paced the poop, deep in self-examination. Also out of habit he kept a weather eye open and without conscious application was aware of the river activity about him. A snow lumbered down-stream loaded to the gunwales with coal. A fishing smack fluttered its sails and changed to a new tack. The Woodside ferry sounded its whistle and berthed alongside the landing stage. A flotilla of gulls bobbed lazily on the swell. The tide must be on the turn for the *Andromeda* was swinging lightly at her moorings. The ship moored astern was also feeling the pull of the current and turning until she lay almost beam on. James eyed her disinterestedly. Another ship put out of commission by a far-distant war. She was of lean hungry lines with tall raking masts and painted black all over. There was a sense of something unspeakably evil about her and every line spoke of her barbarous trade. She'd been a slave-runner, aptly named *Medusa*, and no doubt one or two Liverpool business men were themselves turning to stone at the thought of the efficient Federal blockade. There'd be a few fingers burned in that pie, James thought, and few buyers in that market. He mentally shrugged and returned his gaze to the *Andromeda*. It was no business of his. He saw the figure of Mr Potter walking purposefully toward him. He must make a decision. To risk all and buy the damned ship, or no?

Potter mounted the poop-deck ladder, an insincere smile pinned to his features. James looked across river to the Liverpool docks and as the sun burst through a bank of cloud so the factor that had been nagging away in the depths of his mind broke through. Someone was holding on to his shares! One—or a group—of shareholders was waiting to see which way the cat would jump. It must be so! Otherwise Callon would have pounced long since. He itched to get his hands on the list of Callon's nominees. With that in his possession it would be a simple matter to comb through the company register and isolate and identify the cloven hoof. He had a conviction that it was but one man and found himself with a sneaking admiration for the fellow, whoever he might be. The notion of dealing with flesh and blood instead of faceless nobodies cleared his mind wonderfully. The sense of dejection and foreboding left him to be replaced by a positive euphoria of well-being. He even spared a smile for the obsequious Mr Potter as he handed over his card and gravely thanked the man for his assistance.

He directed the boatman to take him to Albert dock while plans and counter-plans shuffled through his mind like a pack of magician's cards. He tried to form a mental picture of the mysterious shareholder. Evidently of prosperous circumstances if he could afford to resist Callon's blandishments; and shrewd enough to realise that he held the balance. Playing a waiting game, no doubt, trusting that the two principals would try to outbid each other.

The boatman broke into his musings by rowing into the half-tide dock and asking which basin was required. The *Pampero* was discharging in Albert, but Salthouse was closer to the dock road and his office.

'Put me ashore at Salthouse,' he told the man. He would go to the office and stir Tupman into renewed activity.

A snowstorm of cotton blew about the *Pampero* as the dockside cranes bent their necks to draw out white bales raw with the tang of the East.

Baines, leaning against the bulwarks, observed James's progress, then turned away as another spasm gripped his innards. He'd never pass for master. Never in a creation of cats. He was being overtaken by simpering schoolboys who, serving their time as young gentlemen, moved easily up the ladder of promotion as though it had been designed by a benign Providence especially for their benefit. Every man-jack of them had education by the barrelful, but he doubted that one-half knew which way was south.

The shark-headed Mr Armstrong caught his eye and he subjected that unfortunate young man to a scowl of such baleful intensity that the *Pampero*'s second mate hastily averted his eyes and rapidly overhauled his conscience. Baines sighed. Lately the whole damn' world seemed to have gone document crazy. Certificates to prove you were born, affidavits to show you were married, testimonials as to character; dockets, vouchers, warrants. A man could hardly breathe without some busybody requiring a signed testament as to his right. Once all required of a man was that he knew the sea and its ways; today he needed credentials before he could attempt to cross a road. Examinations! Young Armstrong would shortly be sitting for his mate's and no doubt sail through with all the confidence of youth. Experience counted for nothing. Papers was all a man needed these days. Papers. The old days when a man was known by his worth were gone. A distant steam whistle added a throaty dirge to his pessimistic musings. Baines sighed and took himself off to the master's quarters where he could play at make-believe for a few days longer.

James paid off the wherryman and stepped ashore, only to find his way partly blocked by a crowed of seamen and idlers congregated about a gaunt Messiah of flowing beard and wildly semaphoring arms. The man was perched upon a makeshift platform. Above his head floated a banner bearing the crudely painted inscription: 'The Liverpool Seamen's Council'.

There seemed to be a proliferation of such factions these days, more often than not at loggerheads with each other. But it could not be denied that they represented focal points of discontent. Small storm centres about which swirled the turbulent winds of revolt. Should these disparate elements ever coalesce they could pose a very real threat. James skirted the fringe and paused to listen.

The orator was pointing an arm the colour of mahogany toward the mouth of the out-flowing Mersey.

'Over there men are locked in mortal battle over the issue of slavery. Before we applaud, I say let us look nearer home, brothers! For what are we but indentured slaves? Once articles are signed are we not at the mercy of every snot-nosed master, every bucko mate whose notion of discipline is to break your head? Are we not fed on swill unfit for pigs? Are we not paid starvation wages? Are we not exploited by greasy crimps, slopchest tailors, grasping note-crackers, and rascally boarding-house keepers?'

'Aye!' they roared. It was an animal roar, sullen and angry, not the good-natured mob-howl of those who had come to be entertained by a practised tub-thumper.

'Are we free men or slaves?' demanded the bearded Boanerges.

'Free!' they chanted. 'Free, free, free!'

'Then behave as free men! Exercise your rights as free men! Combine against the rapacity of owners and the brutality of masters! Strike for liberty and a new charter for seamen!' A sniff of breeze drove the banner into a frenzy of snapping and flapping and blew the man's whiskers about his head, giving the hawk features something of the mystic aspect of an Old Testament prophet.

A hard-bitten, bow-legged shellback shifted a quid of tobacco into the side of his jaw and spat disgust.

'Combine aboard ship,' he growled, 'and we be charged wi' mutiny, hauled ashore in irons, 'raigned afore a magistrate, and shipped off to rot in prison.'

The rest rumbled aggrieved assent, shuffling their feet and nodding their heads in sour agreement.

'Backing o' law,' said another. 'They gets the benefit o' law, we gets cracked heads.' The speaker was a sadfaced seaman of

55

leathery features and bob-tailed hair bleached by the sun.

Tattered pennants of beard flew in the wind, then a hole opened between grinning yellow teeth.

'Fletcher, my old shipmate, you've seized the eye of the argument; now all that remains is to parcel and lay.' Arms akimbo, he surveyed his audience, then quoted the old rubric: '"Worm and parcel with the lay, turn and serve the other way." In short, brothers, aboard ship we abide by law. But ashore we are our own masters.' His voice rose powerfully to be carried by an errant wind over the heads of his listeners to crews working aloft on ships stacked gunwale to gunwale. It carried to dockers and carters, to longshoremen and lightermen, and for a moment, a pool of silence enveloped the area as questing heads turned to listen.

'There is only one way to bring the owners to heel—pay off, and stay off! We make our stand here, brothers! Here—on the dockside! For no power on earth can make a free man sign articles against his will. We withdraw our labour and hit the owners where it hurst—in their pockets!

No crews, no ships! No ships, no profits!'

'The owners has long pockets and long memories,' countered Fletcher.

'They'll starve us out,' grumbled his neighbour, a tall, gangling man of stick-like arms and hunger-haunted eyes.

'Starve us! How do you starve a man with an empty belly? To us hunger is an old friend, constantly knocking at the door. Not so the owners. They grow fat while we grow lean. We'll show 'em what starvation means. Starve 'em of their profits, brothers, and see who gives in first!'

It had, James thought, the merit of simplicity. But without an organiser of genius it was doomed to failure. The crimps and boarding-house masters would soon put paid to any attempt to interfere with their rich field of pickings. They battened on seamen like lice on flesh with their control of taverns, brothels and lodging houses. With power backed by a private army of ruffians, they were a law unto themselves and held the waterfront in their grasp. No doubt old Noah of the flowing beard was already a marked man and would wake up one fine morning to find himself shipped aboard some blubber-butcher bound for the Arctic whaling grounds.

James had heard enough, dismissed the subject from his mind and walked away from the trumpeting voice and cheering mob. He had more pressing problems on his mind than the woolly aspirations of a handful of sea-lawyers.

He skirted a flock of plaintive sheep on their way to the cattle ferry and crossed the dock road to find an anguished Robert hovering in the shop doorway.

'You are to go home immediately,' he said. 'Anne's been taken poorly. The doctor's with her now.'

CHAPTER 5

THE doctor snapped shut his medical bag, drew up a bedside chair and took his patient's hand in his own. He sighed, inwardly cursing the demands of his profession. It was always a difficult matter to explain. More so in that the woman was a little long in the tooth for a first child and therefore would feel the disappointment more keenly than most.

The long slender fingers, cold as ice, lay unresponsive for long moments, then there was a weak answering pressure as Anne opened her eyes to focus mistily upon a hedge of ginger whiskers surrounding a wrinkled-apple face. She tried to smile, then a wave of pain and nausea swept over her again and she found herself unaccountably weeping.

The russet-apple head tilted to one side and two brown pits opened to gaze down in sad melancholy.

'You should have sent for me immediately.' The voice appeared to come from far away and speak in an imperfectly understood language. She tried to concentrate but her brain seemed fogged and her memory blurred. She had a dim recollection of someone screaming and screaming ... She blinked through her tears and the round apple head resolved into the familiar features of Dr Parslow.

'Pain,' he was saying, 'is part of God's mercy, and we ignore His warnings at our peril.'

She turned her head aside, refusing to believe. 'A spasm. An attack of stomach cramps. It was nothing.'

'The onset of labour pains is rather more than a mere spasm. You miscarried,' he told her flatly.

She wailed into the pillow, wretched and inconsolable, racked with misery.

Parslow moved away and wandered across the room to stare out of the window. In the gardens of the square below a couple of children were absorbed in an incomprehensible game of their own devising. From a house opposite a maid leaned from a first-floor window to vigorously shake a mat in the air while above her head glass panes turned golden eyes to the sun.

He waited until the sobbing subsided before turning to face her.

'You have a fine house, Mrs Onedin, and a husband who cares. You are more fortunate than most.'

'Yes,' she said aimlessly. 'Mr Onedin was always a good provider.'

He dipped his hands beneath his coat tails and cleared his throat. 'And an affectionate one, no doubt?'

She managed a wan smile and tried to make light of it. 'I sometimes think that James and affection are two horses not in the same harness. But we hold each other in high regard, if that is your meaning?'

He shook his head firmly. 'That is not my meaning.'

'Oh?' Her head ached abominably and she wished the man would come to the point.

'I will not hide it from you, Mrs Onedin. On this occasion you have had a narrow escape. I cannot answer for the future.'

He was a shadow bulking the light from the window. She could neither see his features nor, for the life of her, comprehend the meaning behind his words.

Her look of blank incomprehension

made him speak more sharply than he intended. 'That there be no misunderstanding, let me make it perfectly plain. On no account must you bear children.'

It was monstrous. She refused to believe. 'I cannot have a child? Ever?'

His head lowered and shook from side to side. 'I did not say that. I said you must not.'

'Must not? I don't understand?'

'The risk would be too great. For you,' he emphasised.

James, she thought. Poor James. 'But my husband so longs for a son.'

'Most men do,' he answered drily. 'You understand that he must be told? At least I can save you that embarrassment.'

She made up her mind. 'Thank you, Doctor, but the duty is mine. I shall tell him myself.'

He considered for a moment. 'Very well, if you insist. In the meantime I advise that you keep to your bed until further notice.'

She frowned. 'For how long?'

He spread his hands and gave a little Gallic shrug. 'You have a strong constitution. A week. Perhaps ten days. I am leaving a bottle of medicine which should help deaden the pain. You may take up to ten drops in a wineglass of hot water.' He picked up his bag. 'I shall call again tomorrow. But remember,' he admonished, 'you are to keep to your bed.'

She nodded obediently, wishing that he would hurry, hurry away before James arrived, and then she heard James's footsteps taking the stairs two at a time and his voice raised demanding explanations of a distraught parlourmaid.

Parslow had also heard. He put a hand on the door lever. 'I'd better prepare Mr Onedin.' He smiled. 'While you compose yourself.'

'You will remember your promise,' she reminded him.

'Of course.'

She caught a glimpse of James's flushed face as Parslow firmly propelled him back on to the landing, then the door closed and she was left with the murmur of voices, a blurred and indistinct rumble that brought no enlightenment to her straining ears.

A sudden stab of pain made her wince as she dried her eyes and dragged herself part-upright to rest against the pillows. She expelled a long whistling exhalation of

63

breath and schooled her features into a semblance of passivity, then the door opened and James walked briskly into the room.

'Well, well, well,' he pronounced with utterly false bonhomie. 'What's this I've been hearing? Fainting fits and doctors and, and ... such a to-do. Hysterical parlourmaids, household driven to distraction ...' He flapped his bony arms and perched gingerly on the edge of the bed. But concern showed in his eyes as he took one of her hands and stroked it gently. 'There, there, my little Anne. You really must not frighten us so.'

'I'm sorry, James,' she said contritely. 'I know how much you longed for a son.'

His face twisted into little knots and furrows of anxiety. 'It is of no consequence. All that matters is that you recover your strength. I can't afford to lose you, little Anne.' He gave her one of his rare smiles. 'We struck a bargain once, remember?'

She smiled back. 'I remember.'

'In future, no secrets.'

She squeezed his hand. 'No secrets.'

'Next time,' he said, lightly, 'I trust I shall be the first to know.'

She recognised that she would be unlikely to find a more suitable opportunity to pass on Dr Parslow's prognosis. The words were forming in her mind when a tremor of nausea brought bile to her throat and she lay back too weak to formulate the sentence. Beads of perspiration gave her face a waxen pallor. James was at the door on the instant bawling for maids and servants, and the moment passed.

Tupman pulled at the lobe of his ear, enunciated hrrmph in a passable imitation of one of his employer's better-known mannerisms, and subjected his companion to a disproving stare.

'I think you overprice the value of your information, Mr Drummond,' he pronounced coldly.

They were seated at the same table in the Cocoa Rooms. To Drummond nothing seemed to have changed. There was the same steamy atmosphere, the same Temperance posters hanging limply on the walls. Even the customers looked to be the same Dismal Jimmies seated in the selfsame positions as though affixed in a limbo of common misery. The cocoa had the same flavour of sweetened mud and Drummond wondered, not for the first time, how anyone could possibly drink the stuff from choice, particularly with a cheerful tavern not a stone's throw away where a man could sup hot buttered rum to his heart's content in the convivial company of his peers. Provided, of course, that he had the ready. He flicked the folded list of names between his fingers.

'You don't appreciate the risk I ran on your behalf, old man. Should Callon ever find out . . .' He left the sentence unfinished, but, by way of emphasis, dashed a hand across his forehead after the style of Mr Bancroft, the dramatic actor.

Tupman, who had never set foot in a theatre in his life, remained unimpressed. Instead he took out his purse and laid four half-sovereigns upon the table top.

'I am more than confident that you will have successfully covered your tracks, Mr D. If not . . .' He shrugged. 'I am afraid you would be of no further use to us.'

Drummond allowed himself a moment's deliberation to show the pasty-faced creature that he was not a man to be trifled with. But the implication of the possibility of further garnishments was not lost upon him.

'You drive a hard bargain, Mr T.,' he pronounced, and scooped the coins into his pocket.

Tupman took the list and scanned it carefully before looking up and eyeing his fellow clerk suspiciously.

'I trust this list is complete, Drummond? Otherwise it might go hard with you. Mr Onedin is not a notably forgiving man.'

Drummond adopted the hurt look of a man whose probity has been called into question.

'Not worthy of you, old man. You know me. Word as good as my bond.' He pushed his high-crowned top hat rakishly forward and laid a knowing finger against his nose. 'Know how I managed it? By blotting my copybook. What do you think of that, hey?' Tilting back his chair he surveyed Tupman with an air of smug self-satisfaction. 'Blotted my copybook,' he repeated. 'Simply waited until that drivelling old dotard Agnew was making his last rounds, then I crossed a nib and sprinkled ink over the ledger page. Lord, but didn't he go into a bull! Thought for a moment he would have a seizure.' Drummond released a bleating laugh. 'I assure you, he was choice, very choice. 'Course I'd given him the excuse he's always seeking—to escape from that leather-faced harridan of a wife. So— exactly as I'd calculated—he locked me in for a whole hour while he betook himself to the Pen and Ink for his usual gin and hot water and a read of the paper. The rest was as easy as eating pie. It is all there, Mr T., you may entertain no doubt upon that score; and I trust you will so inform Mr Onedin on my behalf.'

Tupman pocketed the slip of paper, rose to his feet and eyed his confidant distastefully.

'Thank you, Drummond, you may rest assured that your good offices will not go unremarked.'

Drummond cracked his knuckles, drew on his mittens and, wriggling his fingers, closed a conspiratorial eye. 'Any further little services of a like nature, Mr T., you have but to call.' He watched the purse disappearing into Tupman's pocket and smiled ingratiatingly. 'To our mutual benefit, I trust, old man?'

Tupman sniffed disparagingly. 'I'll keep

in touch,' he said, and made his way to the door.

Drummond watched his receding back and began to wish he had held out for three jimmy-o'-goblins. He could read that sanctimonious scribbler like a book. No doubt he was even now smirking and congratulating himself upon keeping half the boodle instead of going fair shares as would any man of principle. But, a sprat to catch a mackerel; there was sure to be more where that came from.

Thus musing, Drummond levered himself to his feet and noticed that one of the Dismal Jimmies had greedy eyes fixed upon the unfinished cup of cocoa. Drawing upon the chewed end of his cheap cigar, Drummond removed the stub from his mouth and deliberately dropped it into the still-warm beverage. Then, with the lordly air of a man of substance, the coins clinking comfortably in his pocket, he strode out into the street, to turn instinctively to the nearest tavern.

Tupman returned to the office and spent the rest of the evening meticulously combing through the company register and comparing Drummond's list of nominees. It was simply a matter of patience, a commodity of which Tupman had ample supply. Eventually one name stood alone. Tupman jotted a note, closed the register, blew out the light and set out for Mr Onedin's residence.

A sharp fifteen-minute walk brought him to Huskisson Street where he was surprised to find straw laid across the road in front of number 21—unmistakable evidence of serious illness nearby.

The peal of the doorbell was muffled to his tug and the door opened with such promptitude that it was apparent that the stone-faced maid had been posted in the hall against just such a contingency.

He stated his business in lowered voice and followed the maid's rustling skirts to an oak-pannelled door. She tapped discreetly, bobbed a curtsey and ushered him inside.

It was a large sombre room, illuminated only by the light from a twin-bowled oil lamp and the glow of a fire burning dully in the grate. He took a hesitant pace forward and cleared his throat. There was a stirring from a deep armchair buried in shadow, then his employer rose to his feet. Tupman immediately noticed the tired eyes, the withdrawn look of a man whose mind was concentrated elsewhere. The clerk mumbled his apologies, tendered the slip of paper and recounted a brief explanation.

James thanked him civilly enough and, with barely a glance at the contents, listlessly pocketed the information.

'Thank you, Tupman,' he said politely. 'You have done well.'

Tupman proferred the remaining sovereigns. 'The balance, sir. There was one half-sovereign as inducement and two as payment . . .'

James waved the money away. 'Keep it, Mr Tupman, you have earned it.' He cut short the clerk's stammered thanks and impatiently waved him away.

Left along again, James once more settled into a brooding silence. The house itself seemed to sharc his solitude. He found himself listening carefully to its shallow breath whispering along the corridors to whimper and moan down the chimneys. The room darkened as the oil lamp flamed and guttered, then burned low with a thin column of smoke. He moved across to the table and turned up the wick and as the room brightened remembered the slip of paper. Fishing it from his pocket he read the careful calligraphy without at first wholly comprehending the information. 'Tobias Mitchell. Tea merchant. 18 South Castle Street. 3,000 shares.'

He returned to his chair and resumed his attitude of listening. Anne had insisted that he leave her bedside. 'I cannot rest easy with you sitting there like a crow at a christening.' She had spoken lightly, but he had not been deceived. He'd seen the sudden wrench of pain behind her eyes and understood that she preferred to fight her battle alone. She had obediently swallowed ten drops of the doctor's nostrum and then bid him a firm good night. He had tiptoed from the room, instructed Anne's personal maid to remain outside the door and to call him immediately should her mistress evince the slightest sign of unease. Repairing to his study he had sent for the rest of the household, put them on watch and ward and threatened the direst consequences should he hear so much as a cough. He had then settled himself to wait, his brain numbed with the fear of losing her, until a strange lassitude had stolen over him and he seemed to exist in a timeless limbo.

He was drifting back into that dreamless state of mindless atrophy when a section of his dormant brain fastened upon a tiny spark and blew it into life. Without conscious thought he began to pick at the problem. Rumour had it that Callon was ailing. If so, who would take over the reins? Daniel Fogarty, presumably. 'You are just in time for the wedding,' Albert had said. So Fogarty would marry into the business. He thought of the ship he'd been tempted to buy and a plan of sorts began to take shape. Much depended upon this man Mitchell. A tea merchant, according to Tupman. A tea merchant with three thousand shares and out to make a killing . . .

James awoke to a cold dawn and the grey ash of a long-dead fire. He rose and stretched cramped limbs and the silent house seemed to creak in sympathy.

He took the stairs two at a time and the maid, dazed with lack of sleep, left her chair to dip a curtsey in greeting. 'I've peeped in once or twice, sir,' she whispered. 'There's naught to fear, the mistress have slept like a babe the night long.'

Entering the room, he approached the bed cautiously. She lay so still and quiet and her face with such a corpse-like pallor that his heart churned into his throat. Then he saw that she was breathing slowly and easily, her lips making little pouting motions, and realised that the ghost-like paleness was caused by nothing other than the sickly light cast by the turned-down gas jets.

He moved away to draw back the heavy plush curtains and allow the furnace-glow of the early-morning sun to encrimson the room.

Turning away, he found that Anne had opened her eyes and was smiling. She stretched out an arm. 'Good morning, James.' Her voice was distinctly stronger and when he hurried across and took her hand there was a welcome pressure from her fingers.

'Did you sleep well?' he asked anxiously.

'Like a log.'

'Are you hungry?'

74

'I could eat a horse. Boots, saddle and all.'

He was delighted with her reply and rushed for the door ready to bawl for the cook and rouse the household.

'James!'

He paused with his hand upon the door lever.

'Really, James, I am not so infirm that I cannot conduct the management of the house. Send—quietly, if you please—for the cook and housekeeper.'

She was, he thought, a most remarkable woman. Most remarkable.

CHAPTER 6

CALLON crouched over his desk like a shrunken gnome and choked back a fit of coughing. Every bone in his body seemed to ache. In spite of the banked-up fire glowing redly in the grate, he simply could not keep warm these days. A lifetime's habit drove his hand toward the cigar box. No cigars, Dr Merrydew had warned, no cigars. At first he had defied the edict to his cost, the once soothing smoke now burning and rasping his throat, driving him to a frenzy of wheezing and spluttering until he thought his heart would burst. His hand changed direction and instead opened the snuff box. He took two massive pinches and inhaled deeply. He'd never cared for the stuff, but, dammit, he had to admit it cleared the head wonderfully. Pushing back his chair, he adjusted his spectacles and peered owlishly at Daniel hovering solicitously at his shoulder. He wondered how the lad would fare with Emma to wife; she as refined as sugar, he as raw as a young lobster. But no doubt once the billing and cooing was over they'd shake down readily enough. They'd need to, he thought drily, they'd a long voyage ahead with no haven until one or t'other reached the end. It was a good match, even though he'd needed to pull the strings and practically shove the pair into one another's arms. But no doubt they'd live to thank him for it. Emma secure from fortune hunters and Daniel a power in the land. What better gift could a man offer?

'Everything under command, Daniel?' he asked.

'Aye, sir,' responded his prospective son-in-law and, wilfully misunderstanding the direction of the old man's question, placed a sheaf of papers before him. 'The manifests for the *Orpheus* loading at Huskisson. The *White Rose* is waiting to take her berth and the *South Star* is outward bound on time charter. I am sure you will find everything in order.'

'Of course everything will be in order,' Callon snapped testily. 'Agnew knows his business.' He adopted a more conciliatory tone and pulled his features into a semblance of affability. 'When you take Emma to wife you'll be my heir. I've no one else, so I've made due provision. I've also set aside a nice little trust fund for my first grandson. You'll no doubt find Emma a bit of a handful at first. She's a starchy, toffee-nosed young woman with ideas above her station.' He closed one eye suggestively. 'So when you bed her, bed her quick and bed her well. Remember that you are her master, my boy, and any master worth his salt will lose no time in exercising command on the day of commission. Do you follow me?'

Daniel inwardly flinched at the old man's coarse directness. Although well aware that those of Callon's generation were the products of a less refined age than the present and therefore tended to trample carelessly over the sensibilities of others, he still found it difficult to accept that a father would speak so grossly of a cherished daughter.

He swallowed his distaste and replied dutifully enough, but privately determined to treat sweet Emma with all the gentleness and forbearance of which he was capable.

Callon dismissed the subject, took another pinch of snuff and sneezed blasphemously into his handkerchief.

'Then that's settled. Now to business. I've spoke with this man, Mitchell, and there's not the slightest doubt but that he's playing cat-and-mouse. He'll sit tight until Onedin makes an offer, then he'll have us bidding against one another.'

Daniel shrugged. 'Onedin can't win. He hasn't the resources.'

'True. But Onedin and young Frazer between them could squeeze me hard, very hard, and although I'm of a mind to break Onedin I've no intention of paying through the nose for the privilege. I can wait.'

Daniel brooded for a moment. 'We've heavy investments in sail. If that steamship can do one half that's claimed . . .'

'It won't,' said Callon. 'It's been tried, and failed. No steampot ever built can compete with sail in the carriage of cargo. It's an economic impossibility. Passengers, yes, because people are always in a damnation hurry to get from one place to another. But cargo—never.'

'I am familiar with the arguments,' said Daniel. 'But think on it, Mr Callon. If this ship succeeds where others have failed, in a few years there'll not be a trade route left open to us.'

Callon massaged his chin with the palm of a hand. 'It is but one ship.'

'Where one leads, others will follow.'

'You really believe this to be a threat?' The old man turned his head to stare into the shadows as though trying to penetrate a veil to the future. The wind wailed outside and smoke suddenly backed down the chimney to billow into the room in a choking blue cloud.

'I don't know,' replied Daniel, slowly. 'I don't know. But Onedin's been persuaded.'

Callon coughed and fanned the air with his handkerchief. Falling soot began to drift and settle on the desk top. 'Very well, Daniel. Go and see Mitchell. Make him an offer he can't refuse.'

Daniel stared. 'Me, sir?'

'And why not? You'll be taking over the reins some day, so the quicker you learn to deal with the Mitchells of this world, the better.' He spluttered again into his handkerchief, then looked up and grimaced at his future son-in-law. 'Tell him that if he does not accept I will see to it that that piece of paper he holds won't be worth the trouble of wiping his arse on.'

Daniel grinned. 'Yes, sir. I'll tell him with pleasure.'

Mitchell examined James's card with interest. 'Ah—Mr Onedin. I have been expecting you. I am delighted that you have not disappointed me, sir.' He rose from behind a red lacquered desk and extended a pudgy hand in greeting.

James shook the hand briefly and came immediately to the point. 'You hold the balance. How much do you want?'

The man he surveyed so coldly was a small mountain of flesh. When he sat down he subsided into his chair to remain quivering like some enormous blancmange only restrained from overflowing by the tightness of his garments. The tiny rosebud mouth opened and James realised that Mitchell was laughing.

'You are a man after my own heart. Indeed you are, sir. Direct. No beating about the bush. Straight from the shoulder. I should like to accommodate you, sir, I would really.' The plump shoulders lifted in an apologetic shrug. 'But unfortunately there are other considerations to be taken into account.'

'Callon,' said James.

'His representative,' corrected Mitchell. 'A Mr Fogarty. Do you know the gentleman, sir?'

'I know him,' said James, and permitted himself a sense of optimism. Callon was a veteran scarred by many such encounters and might not so easily rise to the bait, but the touch-hole to Daniel Fogarty's temper only required a well-timed spark.

'On receipt of your card,' Mitchell was saying, 'I took the liberty of despatching a messenger. Mr Fogarty should be here on the moment. In the meantime you may care to refresh yourself with a glass of sherry wine and a cigar?'

'Thank you,' said James and helped himself from a richly carved ivory box. He watched the fat man wobble across the room to pour amber liquid into crystal glasses.

'An initial investment of three thousand shares presupposes a quite considerable confidence in the prospects of the company?'

Mitchell returned with the wine, eased himself gently into his chair and smiled disarmingly. 'I am a gambler, sir. In fact it would not be overstating the case to say that I love a gamble—my constitution forbidding indulgence of the coarser pleasures. Your health, sir.'

Looking around the room James could well believe it. The walls were covered with prints of a sporting nature. Diminutive jockeys on enormous stiff-legged horses surmounted impossible hurdles. Hounds bayed across wild landscapes while portly red-faced gentlemen tumbled into ditches. Prize-fighters held rigid poses. Billiards-players scowled in eternities of concentration. Fighting-cocks rose in explosions of feathers.

James returned his attentions to his host. The man certainly dressed the part. He wore a bottle-green velvet jacket, bright red waistcoat and check trousers. He shaved clean and his silvery hair was so heavily pomaded that he seemed to be surrounded by an invisible aura of highly scented violets. James put his age at around fifty and noticed that in spite of the carefully cultivated sportive air the tiny eyes, buried in folds of flesh, were as sharp as pin-points.

'You keep yourself well informed,'

James commented, and drew evenly on his cigar. He watched the end glow and white ash form while he stretched his legs, and as his body visibly relaxed so did his brain become the more alert, swiftly sorting and shaping the disparate pieces into a clear hard picture. Ships, Fogarty's temper, and Mitchell's instinct for a gamble; those were the key pieces. Mitchell's character should also help. The man was as vain as a peacock.

'I habitually keep a careful eye upon the market,' Mitchell pronounced, 'and when I observed your Onedin stock beginning to move, I thought—aha, someone is bulling the shares. I must confess, sir, that my initial instinct was to sell and show a quick profit. But . . .' He tapped the dome of his head with a chubby baby finger. 'A little bell rang a warning. I call it my gambler's bell, sir. Many is the time it has forewarned me of the turn of a card, a throw of the dice. I paid heed, sir, and enjoined myself to play a waiting game.' He sipped reflectively at his wine. 'Shortly I received a visit from Mr Callon, a gentleman of somewhat choleric temperament, who made me a very fair offer. A very fair offer, indeed.'

'Why didn't you accept?' asked James.

'My dear Mr Onedin, when someone of Mr Callon's financial resources invests time and money in snapping up shares in a company which at that time had not even laid the keel of its proposed steamship, it behoves a prudent man to wait upon events.'

James grunted. The man was as astute as a cartload of monkeys and Callon had obviously overplayed his hand. 'You were expecting me.' It was not so much a question as a statement.

Mitchell looked like a bland Buddha with a nodding head. He spread his hands. 'But of course. Mr Callon's activities must, sooner or later, present a challenge. I had but to wait for confirmation. And here you are, sir, as large as life.'

'You could have approached me.'

'And shown my hand?' The little eyes hardened. 'I treat business as a game, sir. But I play to win.'

The man is a fool, thought James, he talks too much; and was saved from further reflection as the door opened and a discreet clerk ushered in Daniel Fogarty.

Fogarty paused for a moment at the sight

of James sprawling at apparent ease in a chair, a cigar in his mouth, a glass of wine in his hand. He had all the appearance of a privileged guest rather than an adversary. Then he stepped forward and advanced an arm.

'Mr Mitchell?'

Mitchell beamed good-fellowship. 'Ah, Mr Fogarty. I believe you are already acquainted with Mr Onedin? So further introduction will be unnecessary.' He hoisted himself to his feet, extended a limp hand and subsided again.

Daniel nodded curtly to James and seated himself stiffly upright in a green plush chair.

Mitchell pushed his fingertips together. 'Having dispensed with formalities, gentlemen, I think we can come straight to the business in hand.' His Cupid's bow of a mouth squeezed his cheeks aside. 'I hold three thousand Onedin Line shares. What am I offered?'

'For which you paid fifteen hundred pounds with the balance on call,' stated Daniel coldly. 'I'll offer three thousand pounds. Take it, or leave it.'

'I leave it,' said Mitchell promptly, and

86

turned his gaze to James. 'It is with you, sir.'

James yawned and shook the ash of his cigar into an agate bowl.

'Come, gentlemen,' said Mitchell. 'This won't do, won't do at all. May I suggest ten thousand as a starter?'

'I'll see you in hell first,' snapped Daniel.

'That, Mr Fogarty, is a distinct possibility, but the prospect hardly resolves our problem. I propose to sell to the highest bidder.' Mitchell smiled at James. 'Once again, it is with you, sir.'

James sniffed. 'Fogarty,' he said, putting as much contempt as he could muster into his voice, 'will shortly be marrying into Callon and Company, and can therefore outbid any offer I choose to make.' He spared a glance for Daniel and was pleased to notice a flush of anger darkening his features. 'I can assure you that I have no intention of indulging in a private auction simply in order to line your pockets. However, as you appear to hold the winning hand I propose to change the rules and make a sporting offer.'

Fogarty glanced at him sharply. Mitchell's fingers drummed a tattoo upon the table top while his eyes studied James warily.

'A sporting offer, Mr Onedin?'

James nodded. 'One which should appeal to your instinct for a gamble. That is if you are one half the gamester you claim to be,' he added cuttingly, and was pleased to see a flicker of anger in the tiny pig-eyes opposite. 'Fogarty here,' he continued, keeping the same strain of insolence in his voice, 'imagines himself to be a better sea-captain than myself.'

A vein stood out on Daniel's forehead. 'I can outsail you any day of the week,' he snapped.

'Good,' said James. 'Let us then put it to the test. I propose a race between Fogarty and myself. Winner take all.'

'With my shares as the stake?' Mitchell shook his head until the jowls wobbled. 'I think not, Mr Onedin. I think not.'

'Hear me out,' said James. 'You are a tea merchant, Mr Mitchell, and a successful one, I imagine, if you are so easily able to indulge your passion for gaming. The China clippers will be sailing within the next few weeks, so if Mr Fogarty is prepared to back his boast I propose we sail with them and each bring back a thousand tons of tea. Free of freight.'

Mitchell frowned, considering the pros and cons. 'Free of freight?'

'Presently quoted at six pounds a ton,' James prompted. 'You would clear twelve thousand pounds and agree to dispose of your shares to the winner at Mr Fogarty's figure of three thousand pounds. Fifteen thousand pounds in all. You'll not obtain it any other way,' he reminded him. 'For I shan't bid, and Callon won't pay.'

Daniel nodded. 'True. Mr Callon has set his limit at well below that figure.'

Mitchell considered for long moments, then looked from one to the other.

'A race?'

'Which you cannot lose,' James stated, softly.

The fat cheeks flexed into a puckish smile. 'I like the notion, Mr Onedin, indeed I do. What do you say, Mr Fogarty? Do you accept the wager?'

Daniel was thinking swiftly, examining the proposition from every point of the compass, but seek as he would he could find no flaw. Onedin was a slippery customer without question, but this time he had overstepped the mark. He'd no doubt taken a gambler's throw and was staking all on the speed and sailing qualities of the *Pampero*. He nursed a secret smile and nodded gravely. 'Done,' he said, held out a hand and the bargain was sealed.

'We shall also require a written guarantee that those shares will not be sold or otherwise disposed of during our absence,' said James.

Mitchell looked offended. 'You have my word, gentlemen. I am, I believe, a man of honour.'

'No doubt,' said James. 'But I have no such pretensions.' He pushed a sheet of notepaper across the desk. 'So we'll have it in writing.'

They dined by candlelight and Daniel thought that Emma had never looked lovelier as he outlined the outcome of the meeting to an attentive Callon.

'I would have preferred a cash settlement.' Callon pushed away his half-finished meal and pressed a hand to his stomach. 'Food does not seem to settle the same these days.'

'Onedin would have pushed the price beyond reach,' said Daniel.

Callon smothered a belch behind his napkin. 'I'm not decrying your abilities, my boy, but you must give the Devil his due—James Onedin can handle a ship as well as any man afloat, and the *Pampero* is fast, very fast; I doubt we have anything to hold her.' He ticked off on his fingers. 'There's the *Firefly*, the *Barracuda*, the *Cormorant*. Nothing else. I think you've bitten off more than you can chew.'

'That I believe to be Onedin's opinion.' Daniel spoke slowly, letting his words drop as stones into a pool. 'But it is my opinion that you are both overlooking the *Pandora*.'

The candle flames twisted and curled in an unseen draught. The corner clock steadily ticked away eternities of time.

Callon, face empurpled, slapped the table. 'Never! No one sails the *Pandora* but myself!' The effort drew a paroxysm of coughing until his frame shook and juddered like a worn-out machine shuddering to its end.

Daniel waited until the spasm passed and then spoke gently 'With the *Pandora* the shares are as good as in your pocket; she'll outstrip almost anything afloat. Compared to her the *Pampero* is but a waterlogged hulk.'

He could sympathise with the old man's outburst, for the *Pandora* was his pride and joy and long reserved for his exclusive use. Built with the delicate lines of a racing yacht she had served her apprenticeship on the perilous seas of the opium trade, making the run from India to China in all seasons and all weathers. As a young man Callon and one or two friends had invested their savings in her and she had repaid them handsomely. Callon had sailed her into lonely creeks, dealt with warlike mandarins, fought off war junks and pirate lorchas, and after five years had sailed her home with a fortune in specie; enough to pay off his partners and found the Callon Line. Out of a rare sentimental attachment he had kept the ship long beyond her working life. Now richly appointed, regularly overhauled and maintained, the *Pandora* was as fleet and sound as the day she was built. It was Callon's one extravagance and Daniel could readily understand the torment that now twisted the old man's features into an agony of indecision.

He found an unexpected ally in Emma. She reached out and touched his hand and he found himself looking into violet eyes as deep and fathomless as the sea. An intimate smile touched the corners of her lips and she squeezed his fingers lightly.

'Why, Daniel! That means we could spend our honeymoon aboard ship! Such a romantical notion. Don't you agree, Papa?'

Callon snorted. 'Honeymoon indeed! It takes more than a month of Sundays to sail to China and back. Long enough in fact for you to present me with my first granchild.' He took a deep draught of claret and shook with silent laughter as Emma blushed to the roots of her hair and lowered her eyelids like twin shutters hiding a secret room from the gaze of the vulgar.

They sat in uncomfortable silence while the fire snored gently in the chimney throat and candle-lit shadows slid like wraiths across the corners of the room. The velvet curtains billowed and a spatter of rain rattled against the window panes.

Callon's gaze seemed to be fixed upon a distant past; then he raised his head and nodded slowly. 'Yes,' he said. 'The *Pandora* was built for such a mission.' His eyes turned toward Emma with that same blank stare. 'But take good care of her, my boy, she's all I have left.'

To the end of his days Daniel never knew whether the old man had referred to ship or daughter.

Anne, head and shoulders propped by snow-white pillows, lay abed wishing with all her heart that her father would take his leave before the pain griped her again.

Webster sat on a bedside chair, his troubled eyes searching her face for reassurance.

'You've been brought low, daughter, very low.' His hands pinched together, fingers entwining in knots of anxiety. Old hands, heavily veined and speckled with age. 'What ails you, child? What truly ails you?'

Her voice came out more sharply than intended and she was immediately contrite. 'It is nothing, Father. Naught but a woman's ailment. I shall be up and about in a few days.'

Webster shook his head, unsatisfied. 'Everyone imagines that because I'm old in years things must be kept hid.' He creaked to his feet and moved away to inspect the bedside table laden with pills and potions. 'What's this rubbish you're dosing yourself with?' He shook a bottle, peered at the label. 'What you require is a glass or two of brandy and Portugal. That'd bring the colour back to your cheeks sooner than this quackery and mumbo-jumbo.'

Anne summoned a smile. 'I have had quite a stream of visitors, each with their own pet patent remedy. Robert was kind enough to bring a bottle of medicinal wine.'

The old man snorted. 'No doubt after first sampling the contents himself.' He picked up a pill box, rattled it experimentally. 'Parr's Life Pills!'

'From Sarah.'

He adjusted his wire-framed spectacles the better to read the crabbed writing. '"Guaranteed to prolong life, restore the tissues, animate the features and invigorate the juices of the body". Pah! Eternal life at tuppence a box! The woman's a fool!' He rummaged among bottles and emollients. 'What the devil is this? "Daffy's Elixir—a sovereign remedy".'

'Ah—that was from Mr Baines.'

He grunted. 'I can remember having that spooned into me as a child.'

Anne tried another smile. 'It has evidently done you little harm, Father. You will outlive us all, yet.'

There may have been a hint of prescience in her voice, for his sharp old eyes turned quickly to her. 'My voyage is nearing its end, but yours is hardly begun.' He regarded her with concern. 'There must be more to it, for it's not like you to take in sail because of a shift in the wind.'

She answered irritably. 'Really, Father, you make too much of a temporary infirmity. I am not yet on my deathbed.'

He held up a small brown bottle. 'Tincture of opium. I think you dissemble, child.'

'Nonsense,' she snapped. 'Laudanum is an old and trusted specific against disorders of the stomach, as well you know.' A sudden twist of pain made her bare her teeth in a grin. 'I shall be here to plague you for many a long year yet.' The welcome sound of James's voice giving orders and demanding information in one and the same breath saved her from further dissimulation. Then the door opened and he erupted into the room, rubbing his hands together and looking uncommonly pleased with himself.

He paused on the threshold at the sight of his father-in-law, bade him an affable 'Good evening', received a grudging acknowledgement in reply, then strode briskly across to perch on the edge of Anne's bed.

'Well, and how are we today?' he demanded in his best bedside manner. 'Eating well, are we?'

She laughed at the anxiety in his voice, knowing that James's panacea for all ills was a hearty appetite.

'You must keep up your strength,' he told her gravely. 'We cannot afford to lose you yet, little Anne.'

'I am as hungry as a hunter,' she told him untruthfully.

'Good. I have prescribed beef broth followed by mutton chops. We shall dine together. Up here,' he added in the tone of one explaining an abstruse point of etiquette to a backward child.

Webster evidently took it as a heavy-handed hint. 'I shan't impose myself,' he declared in the tone of one long inured to such slights. 'I shall take meself off for my constitutional.' He held up a hand in protest to their unprotesting faces. 'No, no, do not attempt to dissuade me, I am more than content to dine alone—as usual.'

Anne released a sigh of exasperation. 'You are more than welcome to share with us. Isn't he, James?'

'Certainly,' agreed James uninvitingly. 'At any time.'

The old man glowered at his son-in-law. 'The food would turn to ashes in my mouth. I'm not yet reduced to begging for crusts from a rich man's table. Good night to ye both.' He stumped away, a stocky bullfrog figure puffed with pride.

'I'm sorry, James,' said Anne contritely. 'But he really is becoming unmanageable.'

James shrugged. 'A little tetchy, that is all. A long life gives a man much to brood over.' He reflected for a moment, absently picking at a hangnail. 'Perhaps it might improve your father's humour if he were to stay with us rather than spend the rest of his days in that damned cottage?'

'Stay—?' She could hardly believe the evidence of her ears. In truth the problem of her father's dotage had been gnawing at her conscience for many a long month, but knowing of their mutual aversion to each other's very presence, she had hesitated to broach the subject. And yet here was James putting forward the suggestion himself!

'To live with us,' James continued. He spat out the hangnail. 'We have plenty of room and a household of idle servants.'

Anne smiled at James's favourite plaint. He had never accustomed himself to the notion of being waited upon and considered all domestics as at best necessary evils and at worst sponging parasites.

'He'd die in a ditch before listening to me,' James was saying. 'So it might be better if you were to exercise your powers of persuasion.'

'Of course, James, I shall speak to him tomorrow. It is really most uncommonly thoughtful of you.'

'He's family,' said James, and was saved further explanation by the arrival of their dinner.

He ate quickly with his customary lack of appreciation and, with many demonstrative wavings of his fork, outlined the day's events.

She listened in silence, eating slowly and

sparingly, while her heart beat painfully at the thought that he was proposing to sail away alone to far distant China. For the outcome of the race she cared not a rap, having long learned to trust James's judgement absolutely in all matters relating to the conduct of business. Nor did she for one moment doubt that he would have thrown down such a challenge without the certitude of winning.

'To which end,' concluded James, 'I have invested in another ship.' He allowed the suggestion of an impish grin to flit across his features as he settled back to await her inevitable question.

When it came, however, the unexpectedness of her reply took him completely by surprise.

'When do we sail?' she asked calmly.

He showed concern, although secretly delighted with her response. The possibility of a long separation had troubled him more than he cared to admit and the thought of parting from such a remarkable woman for almost a year was a prospect that had filled him with a sense of melancholia quite foreign to his usual indifference to the sensibilities of others. 'In four weeks' time,' he told her. 'But I am afraid that your indisposition precludes your undertaking so hazardous a voyage.'

'I shall be well enough to travel,' she pronounced firmly. 'And I am sure Dr Parslow will readily agree that a long sea voyage would be both restful and re-storative.' Her large luminous eyes turned upon him. 'I should be lonely without you, James,' she said softly.

'Very well. Subject to Dr Parslow's recommendations, mind you.'

She laughed. 'I shall brook no argument from that quarter. Now tell me about the new ship.'

'I saw her a day or two ago. Paid little heed at the time. She is smallish—about a thousand tons—but built for speed. She is called the *Medusa* and has a somewhat unsavoury reputation.'

'*Medusa*? Her name certainly conjures up a sense of evil.'

'She was engaged in an evil traffic,' said James.

Her eyes widened. 'Oh, James! Not a slaver?'

'You must not blame the vessel for the misdeeds of her owners.' He pushed away his plate and picked at a morsel of meat wedged between his teeth. 'All that need concern us is the fact that she can outrace anything that Callon can dredge up.'

Anne nodded. It was true. A ship was but an instrument of man's creation and could no more be faulted for the use to which it was put than could a rope for being turned into a hangman's noose. A thought crossed her mind. 'James—?'

'Mm?' He dislodged the offending morsel, chewed and swallowed.

'Suppose that after challenging Mr Fogarty you had not been able to obtain the ship?'

He grinned at her. 'I put down a deposit first thing this morning. Then after leaving Mitchell's office I went aboard and checked her over from stem to stern. She now flies the Onedin flag; I settled in full late this afternoon. Tomorrow she goes into Frazer's yards for refitting.' He chuckled. 'I'd give a guinea to see Fogarty's face when he first claps eyes on her.'

CHAPTER 7

SPRING was late this year. Overnight a flurry of snow had powdered the city white. Old Men's Beards hung from window sills and spears of ice dripped from eaves and gutters. Horses slipped and slithered on cobbles stained with yellowed slush. The sky was of washed blue and the sea-borne wind cut like a knife.

In spite of the cold Baines was perspiring freely. His new boots hurt his feet and his massive frame almost burst the seams of a new suit. A top hat was clamped tightly to his head and his stomach heaved with nausea. He glanced longingly at the Flags of All Nations with the door invitingly open to a crew of paid-off seamen hurrying across the road; but James, striding beside him, would have none of it, simply gripping Baines's arm the more tightly and steering him to the side entrance of the Custom House.

It was Monday and the notice board outside read:

BOARD OF TRADE
LIVERPOOL MARINE BOARD

Examinations For MASTERS & MATES
FOREIGN TRADE—Mon & Tues.
HOME TRADE & PASSENGER—Thurs & Fri.

Already a few candidates were straggling in chattering unconcernedly and, to Baines's eye, looking like so many overgrown schoolboys. He and James paused at the foot of the steps as the shark-headed Mr Armstrong sauntered into view, hands stuffed carelessly into side pockets, and seemingly without a care in the world. He raised his hat politely, bade both a courteous 'Good morning', wished Baines good luck, then, taking the steps two at a time, disappeared inside the portals of the building.

James took hold of Baines's hand and pumped it vigorously. 'I have every confidence in your success, Mr Baines,' he said insincerely, avoided Baines's doleful expression and propelled him firmly toward the entrance.

The giant looked back once, then, boots

squeaking outraged protest, clumped up the steps like a man trudging to execution.

James watched him go, shook his head despairingly, then turned on his heel and set off for Frazer's yards. Baines would never pass his master's. Never in a million years.

He met Albert at the head of the slipway and together they stood silently watching the progress of their brainchild.

As yet there was little enough to see. The keel sat on massive chocks; gaunt iron ribs pointed to the sky giving the structure the appearance of some prehistoric monster lying with its bones picked clean; keel plates were being laid and riveted into place; smoke-blackened imps kept coke-filled braziers at furnace heat; white-hot rivets curved through the air to be effortlessly caught and hammered home.

Albert yawned prodigiously. He looked, James thought, uncommonly tired.

'I've been burning the midnight oil,' Albert explained, catching James's glance. 'If you will come along to the office I'll show you the problem.'

James shrugged. 'I don't see how I can help, you are the engineer.'

Albert yawned again. 'Indeed, but it is you who are footing the bill.'

They made their way past a paddle-boat undergoing repair. Her bows had obviously been damaged in collision and men were hard at work replacing bow plates and sheer strakes. With the tumult of hammers ringing in his ears James followed Albert around the paddler's stern to the comparative quiet of the *Medusa*'s berth.

The ship rested on the stocks and at the bottom of the graving dock men scurried like ants scraping and cleaning until the copper sheathing, like some enormous distorting mirror, reflected their elongated shapes as mis-shapen denizens of some infernal nether world. James noted approvingly that the ship's entrance was as sharp as a knife while the hollow beneath her flared bows bespoke her racing qualities. They walked aboard across a swaying makeshift gangway and while Albert propped himself languidly against the foot of the mainmast James took himself off on a tour of inspection.

A carpenter's plane whispered over a

newly fashioned spar, leaving a growing mound of shavings to curl about his feet. Shipwrights ran caulking chisels along the deck seams, prising out old tar and repacking with raw oakum, their mates following behind with ladles of boiling pitch. The planking was of English oak fastened with hardwood dowels and as tight and sound as the eye and skill of man could shape it.

James walked aft and mounted to the poop deck. It was abnormally long for the size of the ship, enclosing the base of the mizzen mast and reaching out beyond the deck housing beneath to give a modicum of shade in tropic waters.

He cast an eye forrard. Narrow in the waist and with flared bows, she was a wolf of a ship, built without embellishments and purely for profits. Experimentally he turned the wheel a spoke or two and felt the instant response of the rudder. She should handle well and turn like a top if needed. Satisfied, he rejoined the sleepy Albert and together they made their way to the three-storey building containing the main offices.

Albert pushed open the door to his private office and sank wearily into a chair.

He swept a couple of blueprints to one side and unrolled a detailed engineer's drawing of what to James's inexperienced eye looked like nothing other than an outsize mangle.

'What is it?' he asked, uncomprehendingly.

'A design for a patent steering aparatus,' Albert told him, gloomily.

'Every ship I have ever sailed steers by wheel and rudder. So what is the purpose of this contraption?'

'You have never sailed aboard a ship of this size. The forces in play against the rudder would make her impossible to control by a rope-and-tackle system.' He stifled another yawn and lapsed into brooding silence while James digested the information.

'Very well,' he said at length. 'You are the engineer, so I must rely upon your judgement. I have but one question: will it work?'

Albert stared despondently at the drawing. Voice dulled by lack of sleep, he attempted a summary: 'In principle it is a form of windlass with two barrels over which are passed chains leading down to the rudder. When the helmsman turns the wheel a valve will open or close and operate the pistons; they are so arranged that when one goes forward the other goes into reverse. Yes, it will work.'

He did not sound particularly optimistic. James thought of ships who answered the helm as a horse answers the reins. A good helmsman could sense from the pull of the rudder and the kick of the wheel when a ship was about to pay off and fall away from the wind and so check her accordingly. All these chains and pistons clearly indicated a lack of sensitivity. He shook his head. 'Too clumsy. It won't do, Albert, it won't do at all. You must find another way.'

'The principle remains the same,' said Albert. He cupped his long chin in his hands. 'It's the application that creates the problem.'

'Then you'd better resolve it,' James told him, tartly. 'Otherwise we are going to find ourselves saddled with a steamship and no means to steer.'

Albert's head ached abominably, his tongue felt as furred as a cat's back and his eyes seemed to be filled with hot sand. He really must try to catch up with his sleep.

He would stay home and hope for an early night. Looking up, he caught James's eye upon him.

'Sleep on it,' said James, as though by some necromancy he could read his mind. 'Always remember,' he advised, 'that once a problem is defined you are halfway to a solution.'

Albert nodded agreement and wished with all his heart it were true.

Elizabeth might well have agreed with James's maxim, although her problems were of a more intimate nature and revolved around the delicious expectancy of Albert's return from the demands of that cursed office. Lately dear Albert had taken to working late, often sleeping on a makeshift truckle bed for two or three consecutive nights, only returning in the early hours of the morning for a bath and a change of linen. James was to blame, of course; Albert was too conscientious by far in allowing him to impose so. Really, James took far too much upon himself! Ordering the lives of others without so much as a by-your-leave! It was simply not to be borne! Seated before her dressing table,

Elizabeth brushed her hair into a long golden mane that fell about her shoulders like a silken cloak. She bit her lip in vexation and the mirrored image scowled back agreement. It was particularly monstrous that it should happen at such a time! Just when dear Albert had suddenly taken to performing his marital duties with such an unbelievably pleasing regard for her susceptibilities; so unlike his earlier odious behaviour when that fool Robert had almost blurted out her secret that it seemed like sorcery.

However, that unpleasantness had quite evidently been pushed into the limbo of the past. Young William slept safe and sound in his cot in the nursery and Albert had never again given voice to his unworthy suspicions.

She coiled her hair into a chignon to hang becomingly at the base of her neck, then picking up the scent atomiser liberally sprayed throat and bosom, reminding herself that this was yet another curious feature of dear Albert's transformation. Lately he had evinced a particular liking for the heady scents of musk or chypre rather than her own preference for the more delicate fragrance of attar of roses, or eau-de-cologne. Yes, his behaviour had taken an odd—but altogether commendable—turn for the better. She and her reflection blushed in unison at the recollection of that first quite astonishing night . . .

They had returned from Baldhead's restaurant and by common consent retired early. Naturally they had changed into night attire in the privacy of their separate dressing rooms. Entering their bedroom, she had discovered to her surprise that Albert had turned back the covers. Before she had had time to question the reason for this strange conduct he had taken her in his arms to kiss and caress her and fumblingly untie the bows of her nightdress. Then he had picked her up and laid her gently upon the bed. It was the very first time, she remembered, that they had ever actually seen each other in a state of undress. She had lain still and quiet, blissfully acquiescent to his wishes, but promising herself that she would not offend him by giving way to unladylike movements nor, as sometimes she was wont to do, mewling and whimpering when in the throes of passion. But this had been an entirely new

Albert, for not only had he positively encouraged her to respond to his urgings but had also actually prompted her to utter incoherent absurdities.

It had been a most extraordinary but quite delicious experience and the fore-runner of other equally delightful examples of Albert's new-found gallantry. There was but one fly in the ointment of marital bliss—James! James with his incessant demands upon dear Albert's time? Elizabeth jutted her chin pugnaciously and determined then and there that she would put a stop to it. James would be treated to a piece of her mind at the very next opportunity!

She changed quickly into her new velvet jacket with silver buttons, a bell crinoline of bunched tarlatan, and tiny boots of coloured silk. Then after one final approving glance in the cheval mirror she swayed downstairs to the drawing room to await Albert's arrival.

James huddled for shelter from a wind which, roaring down South John Street, threatened to blow him off his feet. He had chosen as vantage point a doorway in the

General Post Office from where he could keep an eye on the side entrance of the Custom House. Fishing out his watch and staring unseeingly at the dial for the hundredth time, he schooled a rising anxiety by assuring himself that he would not be wasting his time kicking his heels in this damned unseasonable weather were it not for Anne's insistence that she be the first to know of Baines's success or failure.

A letter-carrier emerged from the post office and buffeted by the wind staggered along South Castle Street, his heavy leather satchel swinging wildly from its straps. A sheet of newspaper danced and whirled like some inane disembodied spirit before plastering itself against a lamp post. Beyond Canning Dock the river was a welter of foam and sudden gusts brought fountains of spray sweeping the length of the street, one of which forced James to duck his head back into temporary asylum.

When he poked his head out again the candidates were straggling from the examinations in groups of twos and threes. Buttoning his coat the more tightly, James clutched his top hat, bowed his head and made his way toward the entrance. He tried to compose his features into an appearance of casual unconcern as though he were but taking an evening stroll in weather so tempestuous that no one but a lunatic would venture out of doors except for the most pressing of business.

The exiting candidates increased in number; some wore the downcast look of failure, others imbecilic beams of success. But of Baines there was as yet no sign. Then young Armstrong trotted down the steps, shark-mouth grinning wide in triumph.

James stood in his path and cleared his throat. 'Hrrmph. Am I to congratulate you, Mr Armstrong?'

Armstrong out of habit touched his forelock. 'Passed with flying colours, thankee, sir.'

'Well done,' said James, casting an eye about for Baines. 'If you report at the office in the morning you'll find a berth open for you.'

'Thank you, sir,' said Armstrong, overwhelmed. 'I trust I shall prove worthy of your confidence.'

'So do I, Mr Armstrong.' James paused a

moment before adding conversationally: 'Have the masters come out yet?'

'I believe they finished at the same time as the mates, sir.' The wind threatened to tear Armstrong's hat from his grasp and the beard from his face as he waited politely for his employer to continue the dialogue; although eager to hurry off to celebrate his good fortune it did no harm to be seen in such august company.

The trickle of numbers pouring down the steps increased to a flood. Out of the corner of his eye James caught a glimpse of the massive figure of Baines trailing at the rear.

'Very good, Mr Armstrong,' he said, dismissively. 'Report at eight, sharp. You will take up your duties immediately.'

'Thank you, sir,' replied Armstrong gratefully, wondering to which ship he was to be appointed. Raising his hat in a smart salute he marched away, head in the air, feet on clouds.

Baines wore the dazed expression of a man who has escaped from the tumbrils. He came to a halt and stared blankly at James. James stared back. 'Well?' he demanded impatiently. 'What was the outcome?'

'I come out near bottom,' Baines told him with the same witless air. 'Come out near bottom.' His face creased into a smile of asinine jubilation. He hurled his new top hat high in the air. 'But I passed!' he roared. 'I passed me Master's!'

The hat whirled high to be borne away by a triumphant wind. James reached out and pumped Baines fervently by the hand. 'My congratulations. My most earnest congratulations! Never doubted the outcome for a moment. Complete confidence in you.'

'It was that abacus that did it,' said Baines. 'When it come to sums I just squeezed me eyes shut and pushed them little beads around in me head. It was only the figuring that had me baffled. Passed the rest handsomely.'

He would have babbled on forever if James had not interrupted to suggest that he might care for a celebratory drink and hurried him around the corner to the Flags of All Nations.

Baines, striding ahead, was about to push open the tap-room door when James took him by the elbow and guided him to the captain's snug. 'You've finished with spit-and-sawdust,' he told him, and led the way inside.

The snug was a parlour reserved solely for the use of ships' captains. Deep-water men all, they enjoyed the free-and-easy companionship of one of the most exclusive clubs in the world, membership of which required but the right of command.

There were one or two Yankee masters with blue cutaway coats and silk cravats; British captains in high beavers and square-away jackets; young smart-as-paint brassbounders from the China trade; well-to-do western ocean steam-packet men; Cape Horners with sleepless eyes and skins tanned like leather.

All glanced up as James entered and ushered Baines forward. One or two nodded recognition.

'Gentlemen,' said James, formally. 'Pray allow me to present Captain Baines of the *Pampero*.'

Baines's chest swelled with pride at mention of the coveted title; then his throat ran dry and he stared at James in disbelief.

'The *Pampero*, sir?'

James sniffed and looked down his nose. 'Of course. What did you expect for your first command? A smoke-pot?' Then his face broke into a grin and he clapped Baines upon the shoulder. 'I couldn't leave her in better hands.'

The company, having acknowledged the introduction, had returned to their measured conversation and paid no further attention to the newcomer. But Baines had been accepted. He was one of their number. A shipmaster. From this day forward he would stand alone, isolated from all but his peers by the tyranny of command.

Baines drew in a breath. It was too much to swallow at one gulp, a man needed time to chew over the rind of success before digesting the meat of promotion. The *Pampero*! He was to be master of the *Pampero*! Such good fortune seemed so beyond all human comprehension as to smack of the work of a beneficial Providence. Then he remembered to whom he owed an unpayable debt of gratitude.

'Mrs Onedin, sir? She is well, I trust?'

James held out a glass. 'As well as might

be expected. But recovering quickly enough. She has a strong constitution.'

Baines picked his way over the stepping stones of conversation like a man fearful of taking a tumble. 'Please be so kind as to convey my warmest regards and a hope for her speedy return to health and—and— well I know I owe all to her patient instruction as I never had no head for learning . . .' He fell with a splash into the treacherous stream of verbiage. 'What I mean is . . .'

'I know what you mean,' said James. 'But I think you'd do better to tell her yourself. Only for heaven's sake,' he added tartly, 'when you do, try to speak like a shipmaster, not a schoolmaster.'

'Aye, sir,' said Baines. 'Mrs Onedin'll understand.'

James consulted his watch. 'Drink up, Captain,' he commanded irritably. 'We've wasted time enough as it is.'

'Aye, aye, sir,' answered Baines, agreeably. He threw the fiery liquor down the back of his throat with a practised flip, and wiped his lips on the back of his hand. 'Singled in, sir, and under orders.'

Head held high, he followed James out.

'Captain'—the very word held the ring of authority. There was no denying, it gave a man presence.

CHAPTER 8

THE following weeks passed in a fever of activity. The *Medusa* completed refitting and moved to her berth in Albert Dock to lie just astern of the *Pampero*. James had badgered everyone; pestering Robert and harassing Baines with a catechism of advice:

'Never forget that a master's first duty is to his owner.'

'I shall always bear it in mind, sir.'

'Should you run into difficulties, never send frantic muddled messages home.'

'No, sir.'

'Never get a swollen head and strut around as though the ship belonged to you. It doesn't. It belongs to the owner.'

'Aye, sir.'

'Always hold to your course, but when in doubt play for safety. Make yourself master of the situation and, if in trouble, then— and only then—communicate with us in the fullest possible manner.'

'Aye, sir.'

Baines, beginning to wonder why a man

in command of a ship should be treated as a half-wit, had made his escape to the sanctity of his quarters and prayed for the day when he could put a stretch of blue water between himself and his nagging owner. There was evidently more to being a master than met the eye.

Robert, emerging from the shop one morning, had discovered James critically watching a couple of workmen removing the old simple notice from the wall and fitting a shiny new brass plate with the legend:

Onedin Line Shipping Company, Ltd
Onedin Line Steamship Company, Ltd
Cask Line, Ltd
Shipping Agents
Ship Chandlers
Rbt Onedin (Warehousing) Ltd

His little prawn eyes bulged and his voice rose in a squeak of protest. 'What the devil does this mean?'

'Read for yourself,' James replied, complacently.

'I have,' responded Robert, tartly. 'And understand less. Onedin Line Steamship

Company, indeed! We don't have a steamship to our name, and if Callon has his way we never shall!'

'But we do have a registered office,' James told him, adding patiently: 'It is the law. A registered company must have a registered office.'

'Oh, well,' said Robert, obtusely. 'If it's the law . . . But what of this Cask Line? I've never heard of it.'

'A subsidiary. In practice, the *Charlotte Rhodes*.' James grinned and took his brother by the arm. 'Onedin Line is the holding company, the others are subsidiaries. One ship, or twenty, the principle is the same—liability devolves upon the company, not the investors. Do you follow?'

Robert shook his head.

'You cannot be sued for another man's debts,' James explained shortly. 'Ask lawyer Tapscott.'

'It's beyond me,' grumbled Robert. 'But the one thing obvious is that I am to bear the burden while you are gallivanting off to the ends of the earth.'

'Tupman will take the weight off your shoulders, I shall see to it that he is fully conversant with his duties before I leave. Little will be required of you beyond acting as figurehead—counter-signing the more important documents, generally keeping an eye on things. In short by continuing to act in your capacity as director.' He waited slyly for the effect of his words on Robert's dreams of grandeur.

Robert considered weightily before nodding portentous agreement. 'Very well. Provided I am not involved in the day-to-day working. I do have a business of my own to run, you know.'

'I knew I could rely upon you,' said James, and left him to his dreams.

He strode into the office to find Baines collecting a list of sea stores from Tupman.

It had long been established custom that masters when visiting the sacred precincts of their owners' offices should dress formally in frock-coat and top hat. In fact the top hat had become so much a symbol of authority that few masters were seen without one, even aboard ship. But it was evident that Baines had made a break with tradition, for he had arrayed himself in the full glory of a brassbound uniform manifestly of his own design. He wore a blue cutaway coat with brass buttons and four gold bands upon the sleeves, a Yankee style cheesecutter cap and a white linen shirt with a bow tie. James, who cared not a whit for custom or tradition, was merely amused at this demonstration of vanity. There was something about the very nature of command which seemed to bring to light long-buried eccentricities of character. There was hardly a captain afloat who did not, sooner of later, exhibit personal foibles; bizarre traits to be viewed by the crew sometimes with alarm, sometimes with mirth, but more often with a mixture of pride and good-natured tolerance. Many such were household names: Dandy Dunn, so-called for his predilection for frock-coats and lavender kid gloves; Top hat John Willie, from his habit of wearing a white top hat in all weathers, come hell or high water; Salt-water Jones for his belief in the efficacy of a tumbler of sea water as a cure-for-all; White-ship Williams who carried his passion for all things white to the extent of painting even anchor and anchor cables his favourite colour. Then there were others of more evil reputation, whose blood-curdling exploits were told and retold with gusto in fo'c's'les and bars the world over. And then again an unhappy few who cracked under the strain of command and went mad or took to the bottle.

Baines pocketed his papers and became aware of James standing at his shoulder. He raised his arm in a half-salute, thought the better of it and formally removed his cap.

'You have your orders?' James asked, affably enough.

'Aye, sir. For Valparaiso, round the Horn.' He began to edge warily toward the door, hoping to avoid yet another of his employer's lectures.

'Very good, Captain,' said James. 'I shall pay a ship visit later.'

'Thank you, sir,' said Baines, and hurriedly made his escape.

James took a thoughtful pace or two about the room before turning his attention to Tupman. He measured his words carefully. 'During my absence Mr Robert will be nominally in charge.'

'I understand, sir.' Tupman noticed the stress given to the adverb. Mr Robert was an old fusspot who, in Tupman's view, would rapidly reduce the business to a shambles.

'Naturally,' continued James, 'I shall expect you to give him the benefit of your experience.'

'I shall do my best, sir,' Tupman promised, gravely, and knowing his employer's quirks wondered what was to follow.

James cleared his throat. 'With two ships away for close to a twelvemonth, and the *Charlotte Rhodes* due for a refit, times will be slack.'

Tupman's heart sank. It was undoubtedly true that even with Mr Robert's ship-chandler side of the business there would be hardly enough work to keep a busy clerk occupied. Dismissal loomed before him. He tried to school his features into impassive acceptance, but not before James caught a telltale flicker of alarm in the clerk's eyes.

'No, no, Mr Tupman,' he said reassuringly. 'You are too valuable a servant to be cast aside. If work does not exist we must create it. It is therefore my intention to expand our interests as shipping agents. I believe you are familiar with the nature of the business?'

'Indeed, yes, sir,' replied Tupman,

eagerly. The principle was simple enough: an agent was a go-between. A manufacturer wishing to ship goods abroad would approach a shipping agent whose function would be to find space aboard a suitable vessel. In practice it was a complicated, cut-throat business requiring an encyclopaedic knowledge of both foreign and British shipping plus complete familiarity with a multitude of freight rates. But it was a field of which Tupman had an unrivalled knowledge.

'Do you think you could handle it?' James asked.

'I am sure I could, sir.' Tupman's head bobbed as though at the end of a stalk. This would be work to his liking. Figures were the passion of his life and *The Journal of Commerce* his bible.

'Very well,' said James. 'You shall be in charge of the department. I shall speak to my brother and give you written authority to that effect. You may place suitable advertisements in the trade press and,' he smiled thinly, 'should the volume of business warrant it, you may hire up to two junior clerks at a wage not in excess of ten shillings per week. Your own salary will be increased to twenty-five shillings. You will also receive an annual bonus of one per cent of our commission rates on all goods that pass through this office.' Loyalty was not a commodity to be bought and sold in the market place; on the other hand there was nothing like the bone of promise for stimulating the appetite of ambition.

The clerk's waxen features glistened with gratitude. Twenty-five shillings a week would be more than sufficient to hoist him and his family from the slough of near-poverty to set them upon the firm ground of affluence. He began to stammer his thanks, but James cut him short.

'Just keep an eye to profit, and never buy nor sell at a loss,' he advised, wishing it were possible for a man to be in two places at one and the same time. However, no doubt once the ships were at sea they would continue to make profits whether he sat at home twiddling his thumbs or journeyed to the moon; and work on the steamship would progress with, or without, his presence.

He resigned himself to the inevitable, characteristically dismissed the problems from his mind, and set off to visit the *Pampero*, telling himself that it was no more than an owner's duty to keep a paternal eye on the operations of his hirelings, but knowing in his heart of hearts that in Baines's shoes he would be resentful of such poking and prying from his employer. The truth, he ruefully admitted was that he did not want to part company with the *Pampero*. And he would miss Baines as mate; young Armstrong was skilled and efficient and nobody's fool, but he lacked the older man's solid experience and unshakable equanimity in the face of the hazards of the sea.

James stepped into the street to discover Robert and Sarah standing outside the shop watching a little knot of the curious who had gathered to stare at something around the corner and beyond James's range of vision. Sarah was whispering earnestly: 'Now is the time, Robert. You must strike while the iron is hot. There will never be a better opportunity.'

'Opportunity for what?' asked James at her shoulder.

The pair swung to face him. 'It's old Mrs Ropner,' Sarah told him, breathlessly. 'She was found behind locked shutters not half an hour ago.'

'Must have died in her sleep,' said Robert.

'The rent collector knocked without response,' Sarah declared dramatically. 'He called a passing constable.'

'Who forced an entrance only to find her in the grip of death,' finished Sarah rapidly, as though she had entered a race to be first to impart the news.

Robert stepped back a pace and knowledgeably surveyed the junction of the two premises. 'It would make a choice corner site,' he pronounced sagely. 'A choice corner site.'

'That is my own opinion, exactly,' Sarah stated authoritatively. 'You must not lose a moment, Robert. It is the chance of a lifetime! Do you not agree, James?'

James nodded gravely. 'If you wish to expand, you're not likely to find a better.'

Robert pulled in his chins, squared his shoulders and walked around the corner to single out the rent collector—a distraught pale-faced young man of blotched complexion and Dundreary side whiskers.

James recollected old mother Ropner as

a hook-nosed, wall-eyed ancient garbed in a heap of the evil-smelling rags she daily displayed for sale. Her premises were of crumbling brick and patched and grimy windows but had the great merit of facing the main road and abutting Robert's shop. It was a tumbledown, ramshackle building which had never known a lick of paint within living memory, and of itself would have little attraction for prospective buyers. But added to Robert's premises and with the addition of a few structural alterations it would assuredly make an admirable corner site.

Robert returned scratching his head with the information that the constable had sent for the dead wagon and that the premises were owned by a Miss Simmonds. 'She is of quite good address,' he said, as though this in some way compensated for the dilapidation of her property.

'All the more reason for putting your best foot forward,' advised James, adding ironically, 'before someone else decides to seize fortune by the hand.'

'Sound advice, Robert.' Sarah nodded vehemently. 'You must call upon the lady immediately. Mark my words, the instant she knows that her tenant has passed over she will be at her wits' end. Make her a fair offer—I have no doubt that by the exercise of tact and diplomacy she will readily be persuaded where her own best interests lie.'

'Immediately?' Robert looked down at his green-baize apron and soiled shopkeeper's hands. 'Surely it would be better first to write and request the favour of an appointment? After all,' he added plaintively, 'it is a bereavement.'

'Nonsense,' snapped Sarah sharply, consigning Mrs Ropner to the limbo of those who die unmourned. 'If you change quickly into your best you should be knocking at the door within the hour.' Unheeding Robert's weak protests, she bundled him away into the house, her voice raised in a shrill clamour for Maggie, the slavey, to produce a basin of hot water and polish the master's new boots.

James shrugged, and as a growl of thunder and a splatter of hail scattered the onlookers, crossed the road and headed for Albert Dock and the *Pampero*.

CHAPTER 9

SHE was a formidable old lady with the look of a bird of prey. Dressed in black bombazine she sat stiffly upright in a high-backed chair, one taloned hand holding an engraved visiting card at arm's length. 'Mr Robert Onedin,' she read aloud. 'We are not acquainted with a Mr Robert Onedin. Are we?' she demanded fiercely of a shadow hovering solicitously at her shoulder.

'I—I believe not,' hesitated the shadow.

The claw turned the card over and the snapping black eyes subjected the few scribbled lines on the back to a prolonged scrutiny, as though they were penned in a secret language which only she could decipher. 'Mr Robert Onedin presents his compliments and begs that he may be granted the favour of a few minutes' conversation on a matter of urgent business.' She passed the card to her companion, a thin, wistful creature of frightened eyes and genteel accent. 'What the devil do you make of that?'

135

'The—the gentleman is asking for an appointment, seemingly upon a matter of business . . .'

'I know that, you fool! Business, indeed! I know nothing of business matters. My affairs are conducted by that idiot of a lawyer.' She sniffed, took back the card and resumed her inspection. 'Is he a gentleman, do you think?'

The maidservant, a grey-haired, square-faced female who looked as though she had been modelled from dough, bobbed a brief curtsey. 'If you please, ma'am, 'e 'as a top hat and frock-coat and come in a carridge.'

'No gentleman could possibly write so legible a hand,' her mistress stated categorically. 'If he is a tradesman I shall send him packing.'

'I doubt a tradesman would approach the front door, madam,' ventured the acolyte.

'It is not beyond the bounds of possibility, my girl. The impertinence of these creatures is beyond belief these days!' The dry talons rattled upon the chair arm. 'Oh, very well, Ethel, you may show this Mr Onedin in.'

'Yes'm.' The maid tucked the silver card

tray beneath her arm and hobbled away on bunioned feet.

The old lady placed the card upon a walnut-veneered whatnot standing beside her chair and greedily popped the remainder of a plate of tiny cucumber sandwiches into her mouth.

The door opened. 'Mr Robert Needham, ma'am,' mispronounced Ethel, and Robert stepped forward to single out what at first appeared to be the room's sole occupant. 'I am deeply grateful for the privilege, Miss Simmonds,' he began, only to be halted in mid-phrase by a squawk of rage from the old biddy opposite.

'How dare you, sir! How dare you have the temerity to insinuate yourself into my household on so flimsy a pretext!'

'Pretext?' questioned Robert, clutching at the one straw in a sea of vituperation. 'I am afraid I do not follow you, madam?'

'Miss Simmonds!' rasped the harridan. 'Are you acquainted with this—this gentleman!' The word seemed to stick in her throat like a fishbone.

A wraithlike figure moved into the range of Robert's vision. She had remained so still and silent that he had been quite unaware of another presence in the room. He saw a pale, mouselike woman of spinsterish aspect, imploring eyes and the abject demeanour of one whose life has been dictated by the needs of others. Her hands were clasped before her in an attitude of near-supplication and he felt a pang of sympathy for her situation combined with a compensating rise of anger against the crabbed old hawk with the corncrake voice and the manners of a Turk.

'No, Mrs Arkwright.' Her eyes looked apology at Robert. 'I have not had the privilege of meeting the gentleman.'

'Privilege!' sneered the ancient, and turned her unwinking gaze upon Robert. 'And what exactly may be the nature of your business, sir?' she demanded.

'With respect, madam, my business concerns Miss Simmonds alone. I offer my profound apologies for any inconvenience I may have caused, but I do assure you that my error was not of judgement but of misapprehension.' He'd put that rather well, he thought.

The old beldame reared like a turkey cock and shook her wattles angrily. 'I am not impressed with your excuses, young man, so will you kindly state your business and leave!'

Robert expanded his cheeks and blew out his whiskers. 'No, madam, I will not discuss Miss Simmonds's private affairs in your presence! I bid you good day!' Turning on his heel, he stumped angrily to the door and it was only when he stepped into the hall with the rancorous tinkle of the summoning bell ringing in his ears that he realised his show of temper had almost certainly cost him the premises. Then he became aware of a shadowy figure pattering after him and a distraught Miss Simmonds touched his arm.

'Mr Onedin.' She looked fearfully over her shoulder. 'In what way am I concerned in your business?'

Robert lowered his voice to a conspiratorial whisper. 'Your piece of property. I should like to make an offer.'

The large frightened eyes fixed pleadingly upon his face. 'She—she must never know.'

'Not from my lips,' said Robert firmly. Then a thought crossed his mind. 'The property is yours? To dispose of as you choose?'

'Yes, yes,' she said hastily. 'But you don't understand.'

They heard Ethel's laborious steps clumping toward them.

'Now you must go.'

'But how shall I—?'

'Tomorrow,' she whispered urgently. 'I have a free afternoon.'

She swung open the door.

'Where?' he asked, feeling incongruously like a lover making an assignation.

She thought quickly. 'At three o'clock. The Botanic Gardens.'

The door closed in his face leaving him standing on the steps feeling rather foolish and not a little mystified. Out of the corner of his eye he glimpsed the net curtains twitch aside to reveal a parrot beak and two beady eyes glinting balefully through the parting. He walked away to the waiting carriage to the sound of a querulous voice demanding answers of the docile Miss Simmonds.

It was, he thought, jogging his way home, an odd business, decidedly odd. Companions, of course, were notoriously downtrodden creatures, but dammit, if the property belonged to the confounded woman why the deuce didn't she speak out instead of bedevilling the issue with appeals for clandestine meetings?

Sarah soon enlightened him. 'Without a shadow of doubt this Miss Simmonds is Mrs Arkwright's unpaid companion. Probably an impecunious relative whom the good lady has taken into her home out of Christian charity. Naturally should a companion under such circumstances be in receipt of a small income it is only right and just that she should declare it to her benefactress in return for her keep. It seems to me, Robert, that this Miss Simmonds has been systematically cheating the old lady over a considerable number of years. I am not in the least surprised that she was in a state of alarm.' She pursed her lips, folded her arms and nodded sagaciously. 'Her furtive behaviour is confirmation enough. Yes, you must keep the appointment and if you act with firmness and resolution we should be able to obtain the premises for a song.'

'My own thoughts entirely,' said Robert, and took the opportunity to help himself to a glass of medicinal whisky.

'Be sure to impress upon her that the

negotiations will be entirely confidential, but remember not to part with any moneys, nor sign any documents, until you have consulted lawyer Tapscott.'

'I am not entirely unskilled in business matters, my dear,' he stated, pontifically. 'I think I am quite capable of dealing with a spinster of uncertain years.'

'Uncertain years?' Sarah eyed him thoughtfully. 'Just how old is Miss Simmonds?'

'Oh, thirty to forty, I imagine.' Robert invariably had difficulty in assessing ladies' ages, but a bee of caution buzzed in his head at Sarah's rather too off-hand question. 'Indeterminate,' he added for good measure. 'A wishy-washy type of creature. Seems to be afraid of her own shadow.'

Sarah seemed satisfied with the reply, and the tinkle of the shop door bell saved him from further equivocation. Not that there was any reason for dissimulation, but Sarah, although an admirable wife in many ways, did, he must admit, have an unhappy knack of putting him on the defensive when, in all conscience, there was nothing to defend. Hearing her voice raised in counterpoint to a customer's protestations he decided upon having a second, larger, medicinal whisky before taking himself off to his office. With James apparently as busy as a bee in a bottle someone must keep an eye upon that wretched clerk and apply a guiding hand to the company's affairs.

The day following he took a hansom to Botanic Road and alighted ten minutes early at the wrought-iron gates at the entrance to the gardens.

The sun shone with little warmth and clouds blustered across the sky. A chill wind made him glad he had accepted Sarah's advice to wear his heavy tweed topcoat and wrap-around scarf. Taking up his stance by a sandstone gate-post he idly watched the afternoon parade of nurse-maids trundling bassinets and fringe-hooded perambulators, eyes ever alert for scarlet-tunicked soldiers strutting like peacocks along the gravelled paths. Time seemed to pass with the slow certitude of a sand glass. Once or twice he looked anxiously up and down the road. It was deserted of all but a dray loaded with beer barrels rumbling over the cobbles, a couple of pantalooned girls bowling an iron hoop, and a crocodile of children wending their way from one school to another. Boredly he took to sauntering for a few yards along the main drive, swinging his stick and chopping at the stems of Lenten dandelions that had dared to raise bright yellow heads above the virescent green of the neatly trimmed grass verges. Trees and bushes were as yet bare of foliage except for an avenue of flowering cherries breaking into a flush of wild pink as though given a special dispensation for Easter.

A chorus of ducks squabbling for bread almost drowned the sound of the park clock chiming the hour and he turned his head to see the figure of Miss Simmonds walking toward him. She wore a costume of russet brown and seemed to scurry forward on tiny pit-a-pat footsteps like a leaf blown by the wind.

'Oh, dear Mr Onedin,' she gasped, breathlessly. 'I trust I have not kept you waiting?'

'Not at all,' he replied doffing his hat. Politely engaging her arm he stole a glance at her features. She was decidedly younger than he had realised and by no means as plain as he had imagined. She had high cheek-bones, a rather oval face of pale complexion and large, almost chocolate-brown eyes. He rapidly revised his estimate of her age and put her at no more than about twenty-eight, and she might even be considered as modestly attractive if it were not for a rather prim mouth and head bowed in a permanent attitude of abject humility. Once again he felt a stirring of sympathy for her situation. Then the trees rattled their branches as a sudden gust of wind roared across the park, and as they hurried toward the Palm House the Japanese cherries bowed their heads to shower them in a whirling snowstorm of pink blossom.

The Palm House rose like a great glass bubble from the centre of the park and stepping inside was like passing into another world; a world of tropical luxuriance, hot and humid, with the very plants themselves dripping moisture. Gigantic ferns rose in fans of feathery leaves, purple-stained orchids hung bell-like heads from fleshy stems, date palms and fig trees vied for pride of place with yellow-barked fever trees from Africa, ghost gums from New Guinea and sweet-smelling sandalwoods from the East Indies. Bougainvillaea blazed with colour against a background of dark green rubber plants, and over all was the mysterious all-pervading smell of primeval forests, the cloying sweetness of alien scents, rich, musk-like and haunting.

They handed their coats to a uniformed attendant who appeared like some ancient bewhiskered rodent from a lair beside the door.

Robert, perspiring freely, followed Miss Simmonds, who seemed to be on terms of the utmost familiarity with trees and shrubs alike, and soon found himself nodding formally to these new acquaintances as she introduced each specimen for approval.

'Fine plants, fine plants,' he said, showing the intelligent interest of a man who could barely distinguish a daisy from a buttercup. 'Is gardening one of your interests, Miss Simmonds?'

'Oh, yes indeed,' she replied eagerly. 'I come here at every opportunity.'

'Ah.' Robert leaned forward to sniff at a scarlet flower hanging from a tree of peeling bark.

'That is a variety of the eucalyptus,' she told him.

'Ah,' said Robert, knowledgeably. 'The eucalyptus. Of course, of course.'

'From Australia, and said to be of great economic importance.'

'Really?' said Robert. 'You don't say?'

'Many species produce valuable timber and oils of various kinds.'

'Eucalyptus oil!' pronounced Robert, as though making the discovery of the century.

'And thymol, and menthol,' she added informatively.

''pon my soul!' he declared. 'I would never have known! You do display a most remarkable botanical knowledge, Miss Simmonds.'

She blushed at the compliment, and he became conscious of the thought that for the moment she appeared to have taken on the bloom of some exotic hot-house plant which flowered but briefly to fade and die alone.

They moved along a pace or two. 'And that,' she said, pointing, 'is an aspidistra.'

He smiled. 'I would never have imagined

it. My impression was that aspidistras only grew in pots in the better-class hotels.'

She laughed. 'Or in the windows of withdrawing-rooms.'

They shared the humour between them as though they had suddenly embarked upon a secret understanding, and by the time they had completed their tour Robert felt that he had never enjoyed himself quite so much in his life. Miss Simmonds proved not only a mine of information but also an amusing and witty companion with an unexpected gift for mimicry. He laughed until he thought his ribs would crack when she pointed to a strange beak-like flower nodding darkly to itself in a corner, and enunciated: 'Miss Simmonds, kindly fetch me my barley water,' in a most remarkable likeness of Mrs Arkwright's querulous tones.

There was a circular seat of wrought iron surrounding a tall palm standing in the centre of the building and they took the opportunity of resting their limbs for a few moments. Miss Simmonds flicked open the fan hanging from her wrist and rapidly cooled her flushed complexion, while

Robert dabbed at eyes streaming with tears of laughter.

'My dear Miss Simmonds,' he exclaimed, patting her hand in a quite avuncular fashion. 'You'll be the death of me yet.'

The fan fluttered even more rapidly. 'Dear Mr Onedin. I am most grateful for a truly enjoyable afternoon.'

'A delightful excursion, made the more pleasurable by the company of a charming companion,' he pronounced gallantly, and watched the fan beat the air with the rapidity of a humming bird's wing.

'Kind, most kind,' she murmured, then glanced at him quickly. 'Would you think it forward of me if I were to ask the favour of your given name?'

He pronounced his appellative, adding boldly: 'But I would not account it a fair exchange without you oblige me with yours.'

'Enid,' she told him in a voice a little above a whisper as though imparting a secret information to which they alone were privy.

'Enid,' he repeated. 'A pretty name. A pretty name.' He fished out his watch and uttered a low whistle of amazement at the passage of time. 'I wonder, Enid, if you would do me the kindness of taking refreshment? A pot of tea, perhaps? And at the same time we could get this small formality of business out of the way?'

She snapped the fan shut. 'I know just the place! A rustic tea room close by the gates.'

They collected their overgarments and stepped out into a world of icy blasts from a boisterous wind, and the threat of rain clouds banked against a copper sky.

He took her arm protectively and she clung to him as though expecting to be whirled away at any instant. The wind seemed to understand the game and playfully threatened to blow them off their feet as they proceeded, laughing up-roariously, with the staggering gait of a pair of drunken sailors.

The refreshment room was built of rough-hewn timber in the style of a log cabin, with a notice announcing 'Teas & Refreshments' swinging almost horizon-tally in the teeth of the wind.

Robert secured a table close by the window and ordered hot buttered scones, a plate of pastries and a pot of Darjeeling. 'And be sure to warm the pot first,' he admonished the waitress sternly. 'I am afraid they do not serve China,' he apologised to Miss Simmonds, who expressed accord with his sentiments as to the superiority of China to India teas, but professed she would be more than satisfied with the coarser strain, venturing the opinion that a good Darjeeling owned the virtue of being the stronger and therefore the more stimulating.

Robert took the point, but begged leave to differ, and embarked upon a dissertation on the finer degrees of comparison between such blends as pungent Congou, fine Gunpowder and delicate flavoured Pekoes; between black Bohea and green Soochong; on Ningchow, said to be favoured by the Russian nobility, and the cheap Ceylons, fast becoming part of the staple diet of the labouring classes. Enid, he told himself, might be quite the authority on things botanical, but when it came to tea, bacon or cheese, he was proud to boast he acknowledged no peer.

She listened with just the right degree of admiration to his exposition and they were halfway through their second pastry before he recollected the purpose of their tête-à-tête. He stopped in mid-flow to apologise. 'I am afraid I am boring you, Enid.'

'No, no, not at all,' she told him, earnestly. 'I find your discourse wholly absorbing. Are you, then, in the tea business, Robert?'

'Not exactly. As a matter of fact, I am a chandler. A ship chandler,' he emphasised, in case she should imagine him to be no more than the keeper of a common oil shop. 'On my own account. I also hold a directorship in the Onedin Line Shipping Company. My brother and myself were founders, do you see?'

'On your own account?' she repeated thoughtfully. 'You are then— unencumbered?'

Her meaning was too elliptic for him to immediately comprehend. 'Yes, I am quite independent. I inherited the business from my father and built it up myself.' It occurred to him that he might have given a little credit to Sarah, but intercepting a look of sympathetic warmth from the rich chocolate eyes opposite he hurriedly dismissed Sarah as an unwanted spectre at a feast. Business first, he told himself, domesticity second. Business and sentiment did not mix. Never had. The adage was as true today as it had ever been.

Squaring his shoulders, he bulged his eyes and adopted the air of firm resolution expected of a man who had made his way alone in the world of commerce.

'Tell me about this little property of yours, Miss Simmonds.' Formality, that was the thing. Keep it formal. Enough of this Enid—Robert nonsense. Keep the creature at arm's length. Certainly until the sale had been effected. Afterwards—well there was no denying that in some lights she was not at all unpleasing of countenance, and a man only lived once; she did seem to take pleasure in his company and, unless he was much mistaken, there had been a hint—just a hint, he would put it at no more than that—a hint of promise; understandable, of course; the poor thing, shut up with that confounded snap-dragon, must be absolutely starved of the company of presentable gentlemen of means. Naturally he would not dream of deceiving the child. When the opportunity came he would—casually—drop Sarah's name into the conversation; then, once she understood his situation, he might invite her to dinner, share a bottle of claret, perhaps; in the way of business, of course; nothing untoward; his attitude would remain that of an uncle with a favoured niece. She was endowed with a quite interesting little bosom and he watched its fascinating rise and fall beneath the starched cotton blouse as she embarked upon her story.

'I can rely upon your discretion, dear Robert?' she began, stretching out to clasp his hand, obviously quite unaware of his determination to keep their relationship on a matter-of-fact business level.

He gave her hand a paternal squeeze to indicate honesty of purpose before removing it to ostensibly wipe away a smear of cream from his lower lip. 'You may trust me absolutely, my dear Miss Simmonds.'

The blouse rose and fell alarmingly. 'Dear Robert. You see, if my employer should once suspect that I am in receipt of a small annuity she would immediately deprive me of it, and therefore of my only hope of salvation. I was orphaned at an early age—fourteen, to be precise—my parents died penniless in the cholera epidemic of '46. My father had been something of a scholar—a literary man given occasional employment by book-sellers. Translations in the main, but also pamphlets and broadsides—not to put too fine a point upon it he was a literary hack earning barely enough to keep us at subsistence level. Naturally he had aspirations, and saw to it that they brushed off on me.' Robert thought he detected a trace of irony in her voice as she continued: 'He taught me Latin and Greek and inculcated a taste for the classics; and of course I have French from my mother. I can sew well enough and strum a pretty tune upon the pianoforte and turn my hand to most of the accomplishments of a lady. Unhappily he did not also teach me how to shift for myself: so I thought myself the most fortunate of persons to be adopted into Great-Aunt Judith's household as an unpaid companion. Had I known what the duties entailed,' she cried bitterly, 'I would rather have shovelled coal! I am a slave, twenty-four hours a day, constantly reminded of my obligations and threatened with the door should I so much as raise my voice above a whisper. She is a monster! A tyrant! I could see my whole life being spent in thraldom until the glorious day that this small fortune fell into my lap.'

Robert's heart sank. 'Small fortune?' To what was the ridiculous creature referring? He took leave to doubt the entire heap of rubble to be worth more than the land it was built upon.

'Quite a little windfall it seemed at the time, bringing in seven shillings a week. Although I have been forced to pay two of those to the collecting agency,' she added, sadly.

'Barefaced robbery!' Robert declared, his spirits once again rising optimistically. Seven shillings a week would bring in eighteen pounds a year. He would offer seventy pounds. No, dammit, sixty-five.

She was nodding her head vehemently and the blouse strained until it threatened to burst free of its buttons. 'I know, I know. But I had no choice. Oh, it is monstrous to think that there are those so perverted of soul that they will take pecuniary advantage of one in my miserable circumstances!'

'Scoundrels,' he agreed, averting his eyes. 'You did not think of disposing of the property until now?'

She lifted thin shoulders in a Gallic shrug. 'My mistress is sharp, very sharp, and I have lived in mortal terror that one day she would discover my small deception. So how could I possibly advertise the sale and at the same time maintain the greatest secrecy? I am but a child in financial matters. Therefore, dear Robert, I am entirely in your hands and can only hope and trust that you will deal fairly with me.'

Seventy pounds, he reconsidered. Well, perhaps seventy-five. But not a penny more.

For a moment or two she seemed to retire into an inner dream, then the wistful brown eyes raised to meet his. 'You see, Robert, it has long been my dearest wish to retire to La Rochelle and set myself up in a small establishment.'

'La Rochelle—?' He blinked, at a loss to follow her train of thought.

'I was born and spent my early childhood days there. I am French on my mother's side, do you see?'

He didn't, but nodded his head wisely. 'What sort of establishment?'

'An academy for young ladies of gentle

157

breeding desirous of attaining a proficiency in both English and the classical languages of antiquity. They will also be instructed in the conversational arts, deportment and the pianoforte.' She spoke quickly, as though quoting from a prospectus. 'That was my intention, at least until now, but . . .' Her complexion attained a faint roseate hue and for a disconcerting moment he imagined he detected the lightest pressure of a foot beneath the table. But her gaze remained steady and her countenance frank and open. Only those deep brown eyes pleaded. 'Dear Robert. I should so welcome your advice.'

'Ha-hum.' He attempted to clear his throat in imitation of James, but all he managed was a frog-like croak. He tried again. 'Ha-hum. A most worthwhile ambition, it is time foreigners learned to speak a civilized language. But such a project would, I imagine, require considerable capital?'

'Two hundred pounds,' she said quickly.

'Two hundred—?' He blanched.

Noticing his expression of dismay, she hastened to reassure him. 'Of which I have saved almost eighty pounds! So all I now require is the balance and I shall be free! Free to do as I choose. I shall be my own mistress at last! It really is most providential that our needs should so coincide.' She smiled, showing sharp white teeth. 'Do you not agree, Robert?'

There was no question about it, there was the quite distinct pressure of a foot against his. In fact it had begun to rub gently against his instep with a sly insistent rhythm. A nerve began to twitch in his leg, making the limb jump uncontrollably. It was high time, he thought, to introduce Sarah into the discussion. Then Miss Simmonds leaned back to stretch her arms and the blouse moulded itself into further promise.

'More tea?' she asked, brightly.

'Thank you,' he said, mouth dry as an oatcake.

During the ritual of pouring tea the foot had removed its presence and Sarah's image tactfully withdrew to the shadows. He drank thirstily, dabbed his moustache with the napkin, once more cleared his throat, and schooled his features into an expression of grave concern.

'My dear Enid, you must realise that the

value of a property is regulated by the market and not by a person's needs, however worthy the ambition. I am afraid the sum you ask is far beyond reason. Believe me, my dear, it would never fetch more than seventy or eighty pounds at a generous estimate.'

'As little as that?' She shook her head despairingly. 'Is there to be no escape?'

To Robert's alarm her eyes began to brim with tears. 'Come, come,' he chided. 'You must not take on so. All will be for the best. Look upon it this way: today you will be eighty pounds better off than yesterday; and the worry taken from your shoulders.' Eighty, he thought. Write off five for goodwill! But not one penny more, dammit.

She dabbed her eyes with a square of embroidered cambric and essayed a weak smile. 'I suppose I must needs go where the devil drives. Oh, I daresay I could manage at a pinch were it not for the expense of the passage.'

'Ah,' said Robert. 'Now there I can be of service. We have a vessel that plies between here and the Peninsula. I am sure I could use my authority to arrange for it to drop

160

you off at La Rochelle.' His geographic sense was not of the best but he had a strong impression that the coast of France bordered on the Atlantic. It should not prove too difficult once James was off on the high seas, so he leaned back in his chair, splayed his hands across his stomach and surveyed her benevolently.

'You are more than kind,' she told him. 'For that has indeed been my greatest concern—how to arrange a passage with all the necessary papers and documents without that dreadful woman learning of my intention. Dear Robert, you have quite set my mind at rest.'

'I do not think you need to fear an action by your mistress,' he stated pontifically, with the assurance of one well versed in the law. 'For as your services are freely given no contract of employment can be deemed to exist. I am quite sure that in your case the Law of Master and Servant does not apply.' He was, in fact, rather hazy as to the particularity of the law's application, for it was by no means uncommon for runaway servants to be apprehended and charged with breach of contract by choleric employers.

She shook her head. 'That is something I dare not put to the test. And in the event you are correct, the wretched creature would lose no time in making my life an untold misery.'

'In that case,' he pronounced decisively, 'we must find means of circumventing the lady.' He patted her hand. 'You are not to worry. Just leave everything to me.'

The blouse palpitated delightfully as she leaned toward him. 'Dear Robert,' she whispered softly. 'I knew I could rely upon you.'

'You are a fool,' James told him curtly. 'She is in no position to bargain, you should have offered fifty pounds take it or leave it.'

'I could not possibly take advantage of a lady's distress. I paid a fair price, no more than it would fetch on the open market.'

James paused in his demoniac opening and shutting of drawers to survey his brother pityingly. He shrugged: 'It's your money. What is Sarah's opinion?'

Robert winced. Sarah, in his considered opinion, had been less than kind, and he had also had an uncomfortable few moments skirting around the visit to the

Palm House and the subsequent taking of refreshments. Without actually indulging in direct falsehoods he had contrived to give the impression that the bargaining took place in the presence of Miss Simmonds's mistress. 'An indomitable old lady,' he had told Sarah, after describing the furnishings of the house in the minutest detail. 'Most reluctant to allow Miss Simmonds to leave her service.'

'It strikes me,' Sarah had responded, 'that your Miss Simmonds does not know on which side her bread is buttered. She will soon discover that eighty pounds is not a fortune and there are few opportunities awaiting middle-aged spinsters.'

Robert had hemmed and hawed and ventured that Miss Simmonds had given him the impression that she had the promise of a teaching appointment in a private household. He could not swear to it, mark you, but that had been his impression.

Sarah, fortunately, had changed the subject by hurrying out to examine the fruits of his negotiations and demanding to know why they could not take possession immediately?

'Not until the deeds are in our hands.' He had smiled patronisingly at her ignorance of the world of high finance and at the same time seized the opportunity to stress that he would be required to pay another visit to Miss Simmonds's residence in a day or two.

'Papers to sign, documents to examine, that sort of thing. Miss Simmonds has suggested one evening would be better.'

Sarah had agreed indifferently, only reminding him to be sure to obtain the keys at the earliest opportunity. 'For the place will need fumigating from top to bottom even before the builders move in. I am sure that odious Mrs Ropner was none too clean in her habits.'

Robert had then made his escape to the private office with the intention of consulting James upon a secondary problem.

He fidgeted, watching James ferreting amongst books and papers. 'What the devil are you searching for?' he demanded irritably, wishing James would learn to pay attention.

'The *Pampero*'s sail plans. They should

be of invaluable use to Baines. I drew them up myself.' James yanked open a drawer and rifled through the contents.

Poor Baines, thought Robert, the man must be harassed to death. He hrrmphed, unlocked his private cupboard and helped himself to a soothing glass of medicinal whisky. 'I believe you recently dined out with Elizabeth and Albert? I do not for the moment recall the name of the restaurant— ?' He waited expectantly, but James seemed wholly absorbed in his search. 'The name of the restaurant,' he enunciated clearly, as though speaking to a child bereft of its senses.

'Restaurant? What restaurant?' James looked at him with the blank stare of one whose mind is on other things.

Robert sucked in a breath of exasperation. 'The one with the Frenchified name. Albert took you and Anne.'

James shrugged. 'I don't remember. Ask Elizabeth.' He paused in his rummaging and blinked at his brother. 'Why? Are you thinking of dining there?'

'No,' said Robert hastily. 'No, no, no, no. Just a passing thought.' He swallowed his medicinal whisky in one gulp and reached for the bottle, cursing James for his confounded obtuseness.

James scratched his head. 'It was something like the Rendezvous, or the Escargot, or the Rib of Beef: Something like that. I paid little attention at the time. The jugged hare was quite good,' he added, reflectively. 'Yes, I could recommend the jugged hare.' He slammed shut the drawer and stared absently around the office. 'Perhaps I left them at home.'

Robert's stomach rumbled volcanically. 'Surely you remember its location?'

James pulled at the lobe of an ear, opened a cupboard, peered inside and abandoned his quest. 'Mm? Somewhere in Dale Street. On the left. Stands on a corner. You can't miss it. Yes, I remember—I left them at home. In my desk. I was casting an eye over them only the other night. Baines will be delighted to have them.' He tucked a blue-back chart beneath his arm and headed for the door. 'Have a nice time, Robert. They do you proud at the—what's-its-name— try the jugged hare. My regards to Sarah.'

Robert's voice rose to a squeak. 'I merely want to recommend it to a friend . . .!'

James paused in the doorway. 'Rabbit

pie,' he said. 'It was either that or the jugged hare. Ask Albert.' The door closed behind him. Robert blew through his moustache in a wrath of vexation; then, seating himself at the desk, drew paper and pen toward him and began to write: 'Dear Miss Simmonds . . .'

Actually the restaurant bore the name Le Petit Lapin enscribed in curlicues of gold across the panes of the lower windows and the motif of a prancing rabbit on the scalloped fringes of the canopy overhanging the doorway. It was, in Robert's considered opinion, as he guided Miss Simmonds across the threshold, very Frenchified, very Frenchified indeed.

A bald-headed man with a spade beard and a chain of office greeted them as effusively as though they were long-lost relatives before ushering them to a table discreetly situated behind a potted palm.

Miss Simmonds, glowing with tremors of anticipation, had dressed in her best: an embroidered jacket of green velvet above a wide-spreading crinoline decked with velvet roses, and a bodice of ruched lace which, straining against an unseen pressure beneath, displayed rather than concealed her endowments.

'I received your note—such a mysterious billet-doux,' she told Robert coyly, settling into the chair opposite. 'And on such short acquaintance! I am overwhelmed with curiosity.' She fluffed and flounced and expelled tiny little breaths of excitement as she looked about at the other diners. Robert also cast a sly glance around the room. On the whole they seemed a respectable enough lot: stolid business men discussing chops or steaks; one or two younger men relaxing with a bottle and a dish of kidneys; there were also a couple of sparks entertaining a pair of flamboyant young ladies with a great deal of noise and popping of corks. The dining room was panelled in oak with low rafters, and a log fire blazed in an open grate. The lighting was discreet, the waiters soft-footed and obsequious. The atmosphere was one of moneyed respectability. And yet—Robert's brows puckered in a puzzled frown—there was something else—something beyond the sybaritic luxury of silver candleholders, plush upholstered chairs, snow-white table linen. A sense of other, grosser appetites;

suggested, perhaps, by the leering features of corybantic satyrs and dryads carved into the heads of supporting columns, or the gilt-framed paintings of nymphs in classical poses smiling lewdly at the patrons below.

Robert had an uncomfortable feeling that all was not quite as it should be, decided firmly that if it was good enough for James it was good enough for him, and was saved further reflection by spade-beard appearing at his side like a giant genie from a bottle. The man flourished two gigantic menus and Robert found himself staring in dismay at two pages of incomprehensible jargon.

'Ah—' he said, intelligently. 'Ah— yes— ahem. I think perhaps, the jugged hare—?'

'Sair—?' Spade-beard leaned forward to peer at the menu over Robert's shoulder. 'I am afraid the dish does not make appearance.'

'It was recommended. By a friend,' said Robert, desperately.

Spade-beard shrugged politely. 'I deeply regret, m'sieu. But if I may be permitted to advise—?' His every mannerism suggested that he knew an idiot when he saw one.

Miss Simmonds's head emerged from behind her menu and she broke into a rapid torrent of French. Spade-beard bowed, bowed and bowed again, scribbled rapidly, hissed and gobbled appreciation, and was about to retire when Robert came to the conclusion that it was time to exert his own authority.

'And a bottle of claret,' he demanded. 'Your best, mind. Your very best.'

'Oui, m'sieu. Merci, m'sieu.' The man bowed respectfully and took his departure.

'I do hope, Robert, that you did not think it too forward of me to pick up that man so sharply? But I really do think it an imposition that these foreigners should take it upon themselves to impose their language upon us. That menu could as easily have been written in English.'

'They understand every word you say,' said Robert. 'I was just waiting the opportunity to take him down a peg.'

'I should have consulted you,' said Miss Simmonds, contritely. 'But I am afraid I could not restrain myself from instantly reprimanding the villain in his own tongue.'

Robert nodded approval. 'I could not have handled it better myself.'

'Nor did I canvass your opinion before ordering. I am fully deserving of your censure.' She bit her lip and her bosom lifted imploringly. 'Do say you forgive me, Robert?'

Robert, eyes riveted upon twin monuments of promise, would have forgiven her anything.

'Turtle soup followed by beefsteak pie. I trust it is to your taste?'

'Ah,' he agreed, nodding vigorously and wishing the man would hurry with the claret.

She raised her head and smiled gratefully. 'It really is a most modish restaurant. Do you know I have never, until this moment, ever dined out in the company of a gentleman?'

'Ah,' said Robert, thirstily. 'I thought it better we should meet privately and— um—'

'Yes! I am quite on tenterhooks to learn of your intentions.' She blushed furiously. 'Oh, dear. Now you will think me too bold!'

'Not at all,' said Robert, wondering what the devil the woman was driving at. He was quite sure from the tenor of his note that he had made his intentions crystal clear. He had, naturally, expressed himself with discretion in case the missive should fall into Mrs Arkwright's grasp, but even a child should have been able to read between the lines: 'I hope you will do me the honour of sharing a table at dinner when we can continue our very pleasant conversation,' adding that he would not wait upon a reply but present himself at seven o'clock of Thursday evening and begged to remain her most obedient and humble etc. All in all, in his considered opinion, the latter had been a model of consummate tact. Dammit, she must have understood! He cleared his throat and huffed through his moustache. 'I think we should first remove the obstacles in the way of enjoyment of our meal. Business first, eh? Ha-ha.'

'Of course,' she responded quickly. 'I have brought the deeds.' She dipped into her reticule and passed him a bulky envelope.

'Will you excuse me?' He took acceptance for granted and squinted at the contents. They seemed straightforward enough. A brief covering note from a firm of lawyers stated that the freehold property at 101 The Wapping was bequeathed without let or hindrance to Miss Enid Jacqueline Simmonds. The rounded copperplate of the deeds confirmed that there was certainly neither let nor hindrance to Miss Simmonds disposing of her property in any manner she thought fit.

'Yes, yes,' he pronounced, pontifically. 'Everything seems to be in order.' He passed over an envelope in return. 'This contains a banker's draft for the sum we agreed upon—eighty pounds. I have also enclosed a ticket for your passage aboard the sailing vessel *Charlotte Rhodes*, a letter of introduction to her captain, and documents which should clear you through Customs. I think that should take care of everything.'

'You are the kindest-hearted and most thoughtful of men.' She tucked away the envelope and smiled encouragingly. 'And now, dear Robert, let us talk about ourselves.'

Robert waved an arm in self-deprecation. 'I am afraid I am nothing but a stale old bun.'

'I do not think so,' she said, earnestly. 'I think you too modest of your attainments. Indeed your accomplishments speak for themselves. Nevertheless—' The brown eyes gazed at him mistily as her voice lowered to a whisper so faint that he had to crane forward to hear. 'Nevertheless, I am sure you will agree that there are occasions when a gentleman should throw caution to the winds and declare himself?' She bit her lip and blushed like a rose.

'Declare—?' The word came out in a croak and the palms of his hands began to perspire. 'I do assure you, Miss Simmonds—Enid—that my intentions are entirely honourable.'

'Of that, I am quite sure,' she began, and was mercifully interrupted by the appearance of a waiter in silver-buttoned livery carrying a tureen of steaming soup.

Robert mopped his brow and concentrated his attention upon the waiter ladling out two portions. He dipped his spoon and sampled a mouthful.

'Excellent soup. Excellent,' he announced, and turned his head to avoid her gaze.

'Glarg!' he spluttered suddenly as the soup, defying the laws of gravity, ran up into his nostrils. 'Glarg!'

Miss Simmonds paused, spoon halfway to her mouth. 'Is anything the matter, Robert dear?'

Robert choked and spluttered again and stared through streaming eyes at an apparition standing in the curtained entrance. His most immediate thought had been that the Avenging Angel had been sent to claim him, then, as his vision cleared, he realised it was a less exalted but none the less fearful messenger. It was, in fact, Albert in the act of divesting himself of his Mephistophelean cloak. Their eyes met and held. Mutual recognition was instant. For a moment Albert hesitated, and Robert had an impression that he was accompanied by a rather exotically gowned lady before she whisked her way through a curtained alcove leading to a flight of carpeted stairs; then Albert, arm outstretched in greeting, a rictus grin affixed to his features, advanced upon Robert.

'Robert, you sly dog! I wasn't aware that you also frequented this den of iniquity.'

He had a knowing look in his eye and winked broadly.

Robert, at a loss to understand this unexpected repertoire of nods, winks and nudges, shuffled to his feet. 'Miss Simmonds,' he stammered. 'May I present my brother-in-law, Mr Albert Frazer?'

Albert bowed and saluted her fingertips with the air of well-bred charm he reserved for lesser mortals. 'I am delighted to make your acquaintance, Miss Simmonds. Robert is evidently a man of impeccable taste.'

She fluttered and smirked at the compliment. Robert haw-hawed and wished the ground would open and take Albert to perdition.

'Are you dining alone?' he asked, politely.

Albert raised an eyebrow and surveyed Robert with sardonic amusement. 'Not exactly. After all, you and I are in the same boat—but keeping to different quarters, if you follow?'

Robert didn't, and to add to his mystification, Albert raised knowing eyes to the ceiling.

'Quite, quite,' said Robert blankly,

wondering what Albert could possibly find significant about a perfectly mundane whitewashed ceiling. One of the caryatids supporting the cornice wore nothing but a suggestive leer upon her face and he hastily lowered his gaze. No doubt classical statuary was Art and therefore to be treated with reverence, but some of these figures did seem to go beyond the bounds of propriety. They would never find a place in a British restaurant. But foreigners, of course, were notoriously of depraved taste.

Dimly gathering that Albert had other plans, he smiled relief. 'Then you must not let us detain you.'

Albert bowed formally to Miss Simmonds. 'A very great pleasure, Miss Simmonds.' He was moving away when Robert, not to be outdone in gallantry, called: 'Do remember to give my regards to Elizabeth.'

Albert for a moment stood stock still, then turned slowly, his face whitening with anger. 'And please convey my personal felicitations to your wife,' he said, freezingly, and walked stiffly away.

Robert sank into his chair and Miss Simmonds rose as though at the other end of a seesaw. Her face pinched and the feather in her hat waved in fury.

'You have been most unkind, Mr Onedin,' she said, squeezing the words between her teeth. 'Most unkind. In order to obtain my little property you have practised a most cruel deception.'

'No, no.' He began to feel that every eye in the restaurant was turned upon him.

'Do you deny,' she demanded, her voice rising shrilly, 'that you assured me upon your honour that you were heart-free?'

'No, no,' he stuttered. 'Unencumbered. I meant only in the business sense.'

She brushed aside this weak excuse with the contemptuous sniff it deserved. 'I know that I am but a poor weak creature, ill-informed as to the ways of the world, but it has always been my understanding that no gentleman with pretensions to gentility would suggest dining alone with a lady without first indicating his marital status. No, no, hear me out,' she demanded, waving away Robert's stammered denials. 'I trusted you as a friend, and you have betrayed that confidence!' Hauling up her bosom, she stiffened her neck and stalked away, crinoline billowing to the peril of other diners.

The soft-footed waiter removed the plates with the sly glance of one who has seen it all before, while Robert stared at the tablecloth in an agony of embarrassment, only comforted by the knowledge that at least the deeds were safely in his pocket.

CHAPTER 10

CAPTAIN Webster stood on the Landing Stage watching the *Medusa* slide out into the river to take up station ahead of the *Pampero* which, under jib and spanker and with foretopsails backed, lay hove-to in mid-stream, rising and falling to the long slow swell.

He transferred his gaze toward the Sloyne where the school training ship *Conway* bucked in the wash of a passing tug. One of the last of the wooden men-of-war, she was lofty with a straight sheer to her sides, bluff bows, and lay at her moorings with her double row of gunports open.

'A fourth-rater,' pronounced the old man, spy-glass to eye. 'A sixty-gun Java-class frigate.' He sighed, looking down the corridor of years. 'We'll never see her like again.'

'Just as well,' commented a languid Albert, lounging at his side. 'Just one of those commerce raiders building at Lairds could stand off and blow an entire fleet of *Conways* out of the water.'

The ring of hammers across the water lent emphasis to argument; an argument which, trumpeted in the press and debated at interminable length in Parliament, had given My Lords of the Admiralty many sleepless nights; and not without cause; for within a few short years dreamers like Albert had, at virtually one blow, destroyed the might of the greatest navy the world had ever seen. The days when battles were decided by great ships-of-the line spouting broadsides of iron and flame were over; today the tugboat steaming against wind and tide, the two gunboats being built for the Confederate States, clad with iron, driven by screw propellers and armed with rifled guns firing explosive shells, dictated the future.

'It's progress,' stated Robert, sententiously. 'You can't stand in the way of progress.'

He was standing at a discreet distance apart from Albert and was forced to raise his voice to compete with the shout of the wind. Sarah and Elizabeth, crinolines billowing until they were almost swept from their feet, were waving handkerchiefs towards a group of figures, made diminutive by distance, standing upon the poop of the *Medusa*. They could just pick out Anne's distinctive feminine shape waving back, then the tug chugged past and a swirl of smoke blotted out their vision. The wind tore the black cloud to rags and tatters and when it cleared they saw the *Charlotte Rhodes*, shaking out jibs and topsails, gathering way, heeling and slapping against the tide as she headed for the open sea.

She was no more than a couple of hundred yards off and Robert, with a sense of relief, saw Miss Simmonds standing by the mizzen rigging and staring frostily at the waving group.

'That must be your Miss Simmonds,' stated Sarah, adding rather coldly, 'She is by no means as old as I had been led to believe.'

Robert avoided her glance only to meet Albert's cynical gaze. Albert winked knowingly before studiously examining his fingertips.

'Quite attractive,' commented Elizabeth. 'In a pasty sort of way.'

An approaching ferry boat sounded its whistle as it altered course to give the *Charlotte Rhodes* right of way, and a scamper from the waiting passengers to the raised gangways saved Robert the embarrassment of reply; although he privately concluded that he had not heard the last of it. Never mind, he had the deeds and the property and had no doubt heard the last of that confounded woman.

The *Medusa* loosed her topsails, squared her yards, hoisted her jib, and as the crew, to the call of the chanty-man, hauled on the head braces, she spread her wings, leaned forward and bit into the sea.

Astern of her, the *Pampero*, in perfect accord, filled, paid off and stood out on the starboard tack. Sail after sail spread and boomed in the wind until she seemed to disappear beneath a cloud of canvas. Spray leaping high over her bows, she heeled on the starboard tack and, braced hard, steadily began to overhaul the *Medusa*.

Albert pointed suddenly. 'There she is!' he exclaimed.

The sheer beauty of the *Pandora* caught the breath in their throats as she slipped the tug hauling her clear of Salisbury Dock, far downriver of the *Medusa* and *Pampero*. She would start the race with a lead of a mile or two.

Albert begged the spy-glass from Webster and focused carefully. The *Pandora* had been repainted and, instead of her over-all glistening white, now bore three long stripes from bow to stern: two of black separated by one broad stripe of white, against which were black squares imitating gunports; from a distance she might conceivably be mistaken for a sloop-of-war. She was already filling and running up every shred of canvas she could bear. Albert thought he caught a glimpse of a brightly costumed Emma dolefully waving to the shore, and Daniel Fogarty, arms akimbo, grinning back triumphantly, before the spanker, swinging smartly across, cut them from his view.

He snapped shut the glass and shrugged lightly.

'Well,' he said. 'The race is on.'

They watched until only the *Charlotte Rhodes* was in view, lumbering in their wakes. Then they turned away.

'They'll be gone almost twelve months,' said Sarah. 'Just imagine, by the time they

184

return our little Samuel will be a year older, our extensions will be finished . . .'

'And the steamship completed,' Albert ended, cheerfully, taking Elizabeth's arm.

Only Webster remained, staring dimly toward the river mouth and wondering whether he would ever see Anne again. He was old, the cold crept into his bones, and time was short.

Anne, with her characteristic dislike of departures and leave-takings, had lost no time in taking herself below and busying herself with the task of putting their quarters in order.

The *Medusa* was unusual in that she had wide windows set into the stern which, rather resembling an eighteenth-century ship's gallery, gave a magnificent all-round view, and the cabin a light, airy sense of spaciousness. In the event of bad weather there were port lids that could be lowered from outboard and deadlights to be screwed into position from inboard. A comfortable, plush-upholstered settee followed the curve of the stern, and she could imagine herself spending many dreamy days, taking her ease, picking at a piece of sewing and looking out at the endless panorama of sea and sky.

She balanced easily to the lift and fall of the ship and was relieved to find that the motion did not seem to affect the pain which still, upon occasion, griped her side. The spasms were occurring with less and less frequency and she thought that within a day or two, and with the benefit of clean fresh sea air, she would be able to dispense with her long, ivory-handled, ebony walking stick.

Kneeling on the settee, she experimented with the windows and discovered to her delight that they had been hinged to swing open. Not only would they give more than adequate ventilation in the tropics but, to her mind equally important, they could be kept sparkling clean both inside and out.

She stepped off the settee and immediately tripped over a small brass mounting inset into the deck. One of a pair, she noticed, spaced about six feet apart. She was examining them curiously when James stepped into the cabin, ducking his head beneath the solid athwartship beams supporting the deck head.

'Oh, those?' he answered carelessly, in

reply to her question. 'They are for our stern-chasers.'

She imagined for a moment that he was indulging in one of his rare jokes, but a glance at his face showed that he was perfectly serious.

'Only pop-guns,' he continued reassuringly. 'Create more noise than damage. Brass swivel guns loaded with odds and ends. If attacked from astern we simply open the windows and bang away.'

Anne stared in disbelief. 'Attacked? By whom?'

'Pirates,' he told her. 'The China Seas are infested with the scum. But there is no cause for alarm, I do assure you. We have a quite formidable armoury of muskets, pistols, cutlasses, boarding pikes—oh, and a couple of ancient brass cannon.' He was about to add that they had been included on the ship's inventory, relics of her slave-trading days, but knowing Anne's principles thought the better of it.

'Pirates? Poor Emma,' she said. 'The child will be frightened out of her wits.'

Emma lay disconsolately upon a chaise-longue, fighting to keep down a rising feeling of nausea. The ship seemed to slide and slither across the water, tipping and tilting this way and that, never still. The deck lifted and her gorge rose with it. Then it sank again and she felt as though an unseen weight were pressing her down. The voyage would last for months, Daniel had said. Months! Oh, dear God, no! She would never survive the rigours of the passage; she had never realised that a ship could be so small, so incommodious; such a tiny insubstantial world to be tossed about in the wrath of the ocean. She allowed her eyes to rove over the richly appointed cabin with its thick carpeting, walnut-panelled walls, rosewood furniture and—her especial pride—her upright piano, bolted to the floor as was the tapestry-covered music stool.

The heavy velvet curtains covering the portholes swayed out into the cabin and she closed her eyes, only to become acutely aware of the sound of the run of water against the shipside—no more than inches from her head!—the patter of bare feet on the deck above, a hoarse voice bawling incomprehensibilities, other voices raised in the chorus of a song of such coarse lewdness that she was of a mind to put her fingers to her ears; there were multitudes of strange noises, of creaks and groans, of such a welter of bangings and clatterings that it seemed the whole ship must be falling to pieces. Emma opened her eyes, and the oil lamp swung dizzily across her vision. She groaned in anguish, closed her eyes once again, and tried to compose her thoughts. She would concentrate upon the wedding.

It had gone off very well, she thought. A beneficial Providence had smiled upon them, sending the clouds scudding away so that the sun shone clear from a blue sky and even the wind lowered its shrill voice to a whisper, confining its attentions to plucking at the ribbons in ladies' bonnets and once playfully whisking away a bridesmaid's nosegay of flowers. The service had passed without a hitch and Daniel had looked extremely handsome and very manly in smart cutaway coat, white shirt, high collar and lavender tie. Everyone of note in the shipping world had been in attendance, even to that odious Mrs Frazer, her husband Albert—every inch a gentleman, and so polished and polite in his bearing that she wondered what on earth had possessed such a paragon to even consider marriage to such a trollop. The Onedins, of course, had been there in strength; although their invitations had been sent at the very last moment, and then only after a long tussle with her father. He had set his face against inviting any of the brood, and only gave way when she burst into tears and sobbed that his obstinacy would ruin, completely ruin, her wedding day. Not that she cared a whit one way or the other for the Onedin family, but she tried to think of Daniel and the future; the Onedins were becoming too powerful a clan to be publicly slighted, no matter what one's private opinions.

She had worn a white satin gown with flounces of Honiton lace, a veil worked with falling white roses, a sapphire brooch, diamond necklace and ear-rings; her bridesmaids had been dressed in pink with bouquets of orange blossom; the Reverend Mr Magnus had droned on at interminable length; they had made their responses like a pair of mechanical dolls; signed the register; walked out into blinding sunshine to be showered with confetti and further blinded by the photographer's magnesium fire. It was only at the reception when a garrulous old man with a fringe of white whiskers addressed her as Mrs Fogarty that she realised that she was, in fact, married.

That had been yesterday, and dear Daniel had been consideration itself. On retiring they had, by mutual consent, agreed to postpone the consummation until the commencement of their honeymoon proper aboard ship; and that she thought, dismally, was tonight.

Her stomach retched and heaved and bile rose into her throat as the ship, making a slight alteration of course, brought the wind almost abeam and lay over with her gunwales under. She heard the roar of water, the shriek of wind, tried helplessly to drag herself to her feet, with terror leaping in her throat. Then the door opened and Daniel strode in, looking huge and wild in stained pea-jacket and wind-blown hair. He boomed with laughter at her ineffectual threshing, scooped her up in his arms and carried her bodily through to their bedroom.

Their bed was a large four-poster with silken sheets and wine-coloured eiderdown. He dumped her, none too gently, face down upon the counterpane and, to her horror, immediately began to fumble clumsily with the buttons of her bodice.

She kicked and struggled feebly while her heart thumped painfully. 'What are you doing?' she mumbled into a mouthful of pillow.

'Putting you to bed,' he stated, cheerfully. 'If you are about to be seasick, undressed and a-bed is the best place.' Completing his task he swung her dizzily upright and set about removing her boots. 'Look sharp,' he commanded. 'Off with your other garments.' He surveyed her quizzically. 'Aboard ship a crinoline will prove to be a most unhandy article of apparel. The first puff of wind would blow you over the side. I should dispense with it, if I were you.'

Thinking of her trousseau, chosen with such loving care, she began to weep helplessly.

'There, there,' he said, giving her a bear-like hug. 'Don't take on so, it will all come out in the wash.' He gave her another affectionate squeeze, almost pumping the breath from her body, then, hurrying to a cupboard, returned with a wooden pail which he attached by a length of cord to the bed frame. 'There!' he exclaimed with a satisfied air. 'No necessity to leave your bed, just haul it in as need be and throw up at will. Don't fight it—remember all landlubbers suffer from *mal de mer* for the first few days—so there's naught to be ashamed of. Why, I know quite a few shellbacks who are sick as dogs every time a ship leaves port!' He seemed to think the thought consoling, for he grinned hugely before adding: 'There is little sympathy for sufferers aboard ship; but you are different; you are something special.'

He stood swaying easily in the doorway for a moment. 'I am required on deck, but I shall look in from time to time.' He rubbed his hands together and beamed delight. 'Don't worry, dear heart, it will be a most marvellous honeymoon, I promise you.'

Then he was gone, and she wailed in misery, thinking him the most heartless, cruel and thoughtless man in the world.

Anne had changed sensibly into a serge skirt, seaman's woollen jersey and sturdy high-buttoned boots, before joining James on the poop deck, and was pleased to note that she had found her sea legs, her body already accustoming itself to counterbalancing the lift and roll of the ship.

James smiled a greeting, and young Mr Armstrong widened his shark mouth in a polite grin of welcome before returning his full attention to the set of the sails and the work of the crew.

James raised an eyebrow. 'No walking stick today?'

'I left it below,' she told him. 'It is already becoming more of a hindrance than a help.'

'Good, good,' he commended, then looked at her, anxiously. 'No pain?'

'Just an occasional twinge,' she told him, grateful for his concern. 'Nothing to speak of. In a day or two I shall be as right as rain. I am sure this voyage will be of more benefit than all the nostrums of all the doctors.'

He nodded, obviously pleased with her diagnosis, and took a pace or two to the weather side.

'Mr Armstrong. Let her pay off a little, if you please. We have no wish to scrape the *Pampero*'s new paint.'

The *Medusa* was sailing on a taut bowline, a cable length astern and a little to leeward of the *Pampero*. Anne could see the massive figure of Baines in his brass-buttoned uniform and cheesecutter cap jammed tightly over his ears, standing as firm as a rock on the poop. Even as she looked, he turned, grinned and waved a greeting; then, in response to Armstrong's sharp commands, the *Medusa*'s helm was put up, the after sails began to shiver, then filled again as she bore away and the gap between the two ships immediately widened.

James returned to her side and closed one eye in a long slow wink. 'We'll let Baines get the bit between his teeth. It will give him a taste of confidence if he feels he can pull away from us.'

She looked across at the *Pampero*, bursting with sail and storming down river, her bows cleaving the water into arrows of foam.

'Could we catch her, if necessary?' she questioned.

'Easily. We could sail rings round her if need be. But I prefer him to chase the *Pandora*—I want to see what she can do when pressed.'

He put the telescope to his eye, steadying

himself against the mizzen mast, and focused upon a spread of white sail barely visible, right ahead. 'She's fast, very fast. Fogarty's already set double tops'ls and stays'ls. But she has a most curious motion. Tends to set her stern down. She'll be tender to handle, very tender, and I shouldn't care to trust her in a following sea.' He snapped the telescope shut and grinned tightly. 'It's going to be a close race, Anne. Damned close.'

She had been looking astern, at the Liverpool skyline now fast disappearing beneath its familiar pall of yellow smoke, at the twin shorelines broadening out into the estuary, and at the *Charlotte Rhodes* gamely struggling to keep up but falling back ever further until only her russet sails, glowing in the westering sun, showed her presence. The sun disappeared behind a fistful of cloud and in a blink of light she was gone.

Anne turned back and smiled. 'You will win, James,' she told him, confidently. 'You always do.'

They dropped their pilots at the Bar and, without changing station, swept out into the Irish Sea, rounded the Skerries and stood south and west with a shrill nor'-easter flattening the sea and whipping white tops from the waves. By the following daybreak they were through St George's Channel with the coasts of Wales and Ireland rising purple and green on either hand. With more sea room the ships had spread out in echelon formation, the *Pandora* still in the lead with the *Pampero* and *Medusa* chasing at her flanks like a pair of hungry wolves after a deer.

As Mr Armstrong—with a brand-new sextant—and James took the noonday sight, the *Pandora* let fly her fore-topsail. The *Pampero* promptly repeated the signal.

'Acknowledge in kind, Mr Armstrong,' James ordered, busy with his calculations. 'It would seem that the *Pandora* has sighted the Bishops.'

'Mr Llewellyn!' bawled Armstrong to the ship's second mate, six foot of bone and muscle topped by a long narrow head with round protruding eyes. 'Loose the fore-tops'l! Jump to it! Smartly now, young man! On the instant, d'ye hear me!'

'Aye, aye, sir,' panted Llewellyn, in his sing-song Welsh voice, and hurried to his place at the lee sheets.

The topsail, loosed, snapped and cracked in the wind, then the foretopmen tailed on to the sheets and the sail roared in the wind, then filled and strained forward again.

'Acknowledged, sir,' reported Armstrong.

'Slow, Mr Armstrong,' said James. 'Much too slow. The *Pampero* was at least thirty seconds ahead of us. It won't do, Mr Armstrong. It won't do at all.' He was being a little harsh on the young man, he knew, but a crack ship needed a crack crew, and no crew would race willingly to their tasks unless their officers showed a like enthusiasm. Discipline, in James's view, should start at the top and work its way down.

By six bells in the afternoon watch they had cleared the Scilly Isles and were running free across the Channel approaches, when the mast-head look-out, from his dizzy perch one hundred and forty feet above their heads, hailed the deck.

'Deck there! Sail-ho! Sail off the port quarter!' He pointed and spread his fingers. 'By the count—five!'

James swung himself into the mizzen

rigging, clapped the telescope to his eye and then returned with a satisfied look.

Anne hurried on to the poop and joined him. 'What is it, James?'

He pointed. She screwed her eyes but could see nothing but what appeared to be a faint line of cloud upon the horizon. He passed her the telescope, stood in front of her and she steadied it upon his shoulder. As she focused the cloud resolved into a series of white daubs coming closer and closer.

'Ships!' she exclaimed. 'A line of ships!' She blinked at him. 'But what is so extraordinary about a number of ships in the Channel? You have often claimed it to be the busiest seaway in the world.'

'Wait and see,' he told her. Then, to Mr Armstrong hovering nervously at his shoulder: 'Very well, Mr Armstrong. Let fly the fore-tops'l.'

'Fore-tops'l Mr Llewellyn!' bellowed Armstrong, and Mr Llewellyn, who had been equally nervously keeping close to the row of belaying pins, screeched 'Cast off!' to a grinning able-seaman stationed at the weather sheets for such an emergency.

The ropes hissed through the blocks and the topsail fluttered in the wind.

Armstrong was squinting toward the *Pampero*. '*Pampero* acknowledges, sir,' he reported, adding on a note of satisfaction: 'Forty seconds, sir.'

'Thank you, Mr Armstrong,' answered James, gravely. He pocketed his watch. 'The *Pandora* was also a little behind. I gave her thirty-five seconds. Carry on, if you please.'

Within half an hour the approaching ships could be individually distinguished as clouds of sail storming down Channel, racing neck and neck, almost yard-arm to yard-arm, fountains of spray bursting over their bows, every sail humming taut as a bowstring.

Anne caught her breath. 'What are they?' she whispered, as though raising her voice would break a magic spell.

James, examining their rigs, spelled them off. '*Fiery Cross, Flying Spur, Falcon, Ellen Rodger, Challenger*. The China tea fleet,' he told her. 'The fastest ships in the world.'

They waited a little longer until the ships loomed large and clear and they could hear the howl of wind through rigging, the tearing rush of bows through water.

'Very well, Mr Armstrong,' said James, at length. 'Bring her round if you please. Steer west by south.'

He put an arm around Anne's shoulders and his face split into the near-boyish grin that always made her heart jump. 'We'll lead the pack.'

As the *Medusa*'s yards came round the advancing fleet seemed to dance astern. James took a turn or two about the poop, glanced up at the set of the sails, cocked an eye at the sky and golden tufts of clouds shimmering in the sun. He cleared his throat.

'Mr Armstrong!'

'Aye, sir?'

'I think it time to put her through her paces. Let us see what she can bear, shall we?'

'Aye, aye, sir!' responded Armstrong, enthusiastically, bawling immediately: 'Second mate! Bos'n! All hands! All hands! All hands to make sail! Bos'n—roust out cook and idlers. I want no farmers on this ship, d'ye hear me! T'gallants and spencers! Jump to it! Tacks and sheets! Smartly now!'

He'd do, thought James. Yes, Mr Armstrong would do very well indeed!

The *Medusa* bloomed with sails. The cook, a black-as-night negro, greasy apron flapping in the breeze, had taken up his station at the fore-sheet and, cursing and swearing, was heaving and hauling with the rest. The carpenter, a mournful Scot of ear-shattering accent, clung ferociously to the weather tack of the main course until the line, tightening, swung his feet clear of the deck. A sea, bursting over the bows, sent the bearded sailmaker coughing and spluttering into the scuppers, from which he arose like some latter-day Moses to howl imprecations at the sea and all its sons.

The *Medusa* reached forward, gathered herself, and seemed to hiss through the sea. James took the wheel from the helmsman and tested her response to the rudder. The ship reacted like a thing alive, answering the merest touch with a skittish flirt of the head, and he could feel the tremor of the rudder blade kicking against the run of the sea as he eased the helm a shade.

'She carries about a quarter turn o'

weather 'ellum, sir,' ventured the helmsman, helpfully.

James nodded, eyes fixed on the headsails already beginning to shiver, while his right hand fingered the carved, brass-mounted centre-spoke of the wheel now no more than a spoke from the midships position. He put the helm up and the sails drew full and firm once again.

'We'll try fore and main royals, if you please, Mr Armstrong,' he called.

He watched the hands racing aloft to lay out on the yard-arms and cast off the gaskets, while his brain busied itself with the sort of problem he enjoyed. It had, to his mind, all the beauty of a mathematical equation, with the sea and wind as variables: a ship needed to be stowed and trimmed so that she was balanced equally about an imaginary point of rotation—ideally a little aft of centre—and not be obliged to carry her rudder much off the line of the keel, which would then tend to act as a drag upon her way, and carry her head into, or away from, the wind. The solution for a weatherly ship, such as the *Medusa*, was to either take in sail aft, or increase the head sails. But too much head sail and the wind pressure would tend to force her head down and therefore cause her to carry even more weather helm than before. It was a fine balance of forces requiring nicety of judgement.

The fore royal shook loose, the job watch on deck hauled away on sheets and tacks while others tailed on to the braces. The helm began to ease of its own accord. The main royal followed suit and James brought the centre spoke to midships before relinquishing the wheel to the helmsman and strolling casually away, elaborately unconscious of Mr Armstrong's wide-eyed stare of admiration.

Once clear of the chops of the Channel the accompanying ships spread out into a fan of white plumes. Keay's *Falcon*, edging into the lead, rapidly overhauled the *Medusa* and, braced sharp on the port tack, creamed past in a welter of foam and spray, while James enviously watched the self-reliant discipline of her crew, every man at his appointed place, pulling and hauling, trimming yards as though motivated by a common will. These were the famed China-birds; arrogant, fiercely jealous of the reputation of their ships, every seaman able, not only to hand, reef and steer, but also knot, point, splice, parcel and serve, turn in a dead-eye, fish a topmast or set up standing rigging. He spared a glance for his own crew; he had chosen with care, picked the best the waterfront had to offer; they were young, willing, obedient to orders, but they lacked the *esprit de corps* of the *Falcon*'s crew.

Captain Keay of the *Falcon*, a dapper man of high forehead, pointed beard jutting forward and dressed in top hat, frock-coat and bow tie, was standing on the poop, hands clasped behind him, feet spread apart, balanced easily against the cant of the deck. James, on impulse, removed his own top hat, waved and pointed at it.

Keay turned his head and for a moment surveyed them gravely. Then he bowed, bowed again to Anne, and raised his own hat in acknowledgement.

'What did that mean?' asked Anne.

'I've just wagered a new top hat that we shall be first into Foochow,' James told her.

She frowned. 'But surely we could not possibly compete?'

James grinned at her. 'It's worth a top hat. Look at the crew.'

The bos'n, a barrel-chested, bow-legged veteran, once a foreman rigger ashore, was waving at his counterpart aboard the *Falcon*.

'He's just bet a month's pay,' said James.

Anne looked along the deck and then aloft. Every man aboard seemed to have been infected with madness. All were shouting, waving, jeering good-naturedly; all had taken up the challenge.

'Now,' said James, softly, 'we can work 'em until they drop.'

Night chased day across the sky and ships' lights winked like fireflies. Stars burned like fragments of blue ice and a full moon rose to cast a curious, dream-like radiance over the sleeping sea.

By the first flush of morning there wasn't a ship in sight. The wind had dropped to a steady cool breeze coming in over the quarter, the sea stretched toward the barely visible horizon in long smooth curls, while the ship rose and fell, rose and fell with a somnolent, sleep-inducing motion.

Mr Llewellyn, propped half-asleep

against the taffrail, was therefore startled out of his wits when a quiet voice, not a yard from his shoulder, said politely: 'I should be obliged for your attention, Mr Llewellyn. Wear ship, if you please.'

'Sir?' Llewellyn came fully awake instantly, threw a hurried glance up at the set of the sails, then around the empty horizon, and finally gaped at the apparition waiting patiently before him.

'Sir?' He sounded as though he could not believe the evidence of his ears.

'I trust, Mr Llewellyn,' said James, coldly, 'that I shall never again be required to repeat an order. Stand by to wear ship, I said.'

'Aye, aye, sir,' answered the dazed Llewellyn. He hurried to the break of the poop and called down weakly to the job watch, lounging on deck and waiting for four bells when they would commence their daily routine of scrubbing and washing down the decks.

'All hands. Stand by to wear ship.'

They, too, stood uncertainly, looking aft at the originator of this eccentric order.

'You are issuing a command, not a request, Mr Llewellyn.'

James's bleak tones galvanised the second mate to life.

'Stand by to come about! All hands to wear ship! All hands!' he yelled.

Someone broke away and made a shambling run for the fo'c's'le, poked his head inside the scuttle and called down to the watch below.

They came tumbling on to deck, rubbing sleep from their eyes, bewildered at this sudden emergency.

'They behave like a bunch of sheep,' snapped James. 'Liven 'em up, Mr Llewellyn.'

'Move!' bawled Llewellyn. 'Jump to it! Smartly now! Bos'n—shake a bit of life into them!' His sing-song Welsh voice rose to high pitch as though on the edge of hysteria. He glanced at his captain uncertainly, then hesitantly.

'No, Mr Llewellyn,' said James, gently. 'You are the officer of the watch. I am asleep below, and there is a reef right ahead.'

'Reef . . .?' Llewellyn, slow to react, blinked. There were no reefs in the north Atlantic.

'You may put up the helm, and carry on,' said James. He took his watch from his pocket and gazed at the dial. 'Carry on,' he repeated, and waited patiently while, to a tumult of shouts and curses, the hands tailed on to braces and downhauls and the ship slowly lumbered around in a wide circle.

'She behaved like a lame carthorse,' James commented, snapping shut his watch case. 'Twenty-five minutes, Mr Llewellyn. Had there been a reef we would have been high and dry long since. Captain Keay claims he can wear ship in ten minutes—from the time of giving the order to the last line being flaked down. I intend to better that time. So once again, if you please, Mr Llewellyn. And again, and again, and again, until we have it right.'

All morning they worked and slaved and swore and hated that cold figure slowly pacing the quarterdeck, watch in hand, pale blue eyes merciless. And the ship gyrated as though engaged in some idiot's dance, round and round and round, ploughing through her own wake, chasing her own tail over and over again, until they thought they would go mad. Sobbing with exhaustion they waited yet again for the hated command, while the sun rose over the yard-arm and seemed to stand still in the southern sky.

'Thirteen minutes,' said James. 'We are improving. Very well, Mr Llewellyn, you may send the hands to breakfast. We shall resume in the afternoon watch.'

'Aye, aye, sir,' answered Llewellyn, hoarse-voiced and dazed, only grateful that it would be Mr Armstrong's watch.

Anne plucked at James's sleeve. 'James—won't all this manoeuvring lose us valuable time? The *Pandora* must be half a day's run ahead by now.'

James smiled at her. 'The race does not always go to the swift, my dear. Sometimes it goes to the cunning.'

CHAPTER 11

ONCE James was safely out of the way, Callon struck swiftly, and a mystified Albert consulted Robert. 'He has called an emergency meeting of shareholders to discuss the progress of the steamship. I cannot for the life of me see what he hopes to gain. You do hold James's proxy votes?' he asked, anxiously.

'Of course,' said Robert. 'James trusts me absolutely.' He refrained from adding that James had also warned him of the dire consequences of their misuse. 'Never fear, combined we can outvote Callon on any issue he cares to raise.'

Albert uneasily fingered his moustache. 'There's more to it than meets the eye.'

They had met in the private office and in a moment of silence they could hear Tupman's pen scratching away as he diligently employed himself about the agency side of the business. Robert swivelled idly in his chair and drummed his fingers upon the desk top, before raising the matter uppermost in his mind.

'Ah—about that restaurant,' he began.

Albert turned away from a brooding inspection of a row of chimney pots outlined against the dusty windows, and grinned at Robert.

'You are the slyest of dogs! And all this time I thought you a pillar of rectitude! But you really must learn to be more discreet. One does not bandy the name of one's wife about a place of assignation.'

'A place of—what?'

'Oh, come, Robert—don't play the innocent with me. Where on earth did you find such a delectable creature? She carried a most handsome pair of Delilahs, I noticed.'

'Delilahs?' Robert floundered, lost.

Albert's hands waved unmistakable shapes in the air and he winked broadly. 'Nature's sweet endowments. Sorry I was rather sharp with you, but you caught me on a short rein—I had not realised that that was your first canter.'

Robert flapped an indignant hand. 'I assure you that in my relationship with Miss Simmonds the proprieties were at all times observed.'

'Of course,' Albert agreed, soothingly. 'Have you told Sarah?'

'Well, no, not exactly. Not that I have anything to hide, but . . .'

'But wives can be somewhat contumacious where the seat of affections is concerned,' Albert finished for him. 'I quite understand. However, you may be sure that your secret is as safe with me, as mine with you.'

'Ah,' said Robert, more and more baffled.

Albert perched on the edge of the desk, selected one of Robert's cigars and blew out a cloud of smoke. 'Furthermore you may trust Henri's discretion absolutely. I once put it to the test by dining with Elizabeth, Anne and James. Henri never so much as batted an eye. I found it quite added the spice of danger to the sauce of intrigue, if you follow?'

Robert didn't, wondered who on earth was Onri, then decided not to pursue the matter further, but let sleeping dogs lie.

Albert also seemed to dismiss the subject from his mind for he slid off the desk, stretched his arms and yawned. 'In view of

James's absence, I think it might be as well if you were to chair the meeting.'

'Of course, of course,' said Robert, swelling his chest. 'You may rely upon me.'

'I must,' said Albert, resignedly. 'For there is no one else. No doubt I shall be kept busy answering Callon's tomfool questions, but I'll offer all the support I can. Just remember to be firm, familiarise yourself with the rules, and all should be well.'

'I think I know how to conduct the office of chairman,' Robert grunted, irritably.

Cigar clenched between his teeth, Albert slowly paced the room. 'Callon's an old fox,' he muttered. 'He's up to something.'

The meeting was held in the Mechanics Institute, especially hired for the purpose. It was a bare hall, with a few chairs and wooden benches facing a raised dais upon which stood a cloth-covered trestle table and behind which sat Robert and Albert. In front of Robert were the company's register, articles of association, a carafe of water, a couple of glass tumblers and a gavel. Albert sat at Robert's left hand and Tupman, co-opted as secretary, at his right. Thus equipped and supported, and fortified with the additional stimulus of a glass of medicinal whisky nestling comfortably in his stomach, Robert felt confident enough to face a dozen Callons.

Albert had prepared himself for the meeting by bringing along not only outline plans and detailed engineering drawings, but also a scale model of the proposed ship. This model stood upon a small table in front of the dais and the shareholders were filing past to subject it to close scrutiny. Few seemed happy with their inspection.

'She's an ugly brute,' said one.

'Where the devil are her masts?' asked another.

Albert was leaning back in his chair, hands clasped behind his head, as though half asleep.

Callon stood back, wagging his head despairingly. 'Looks damned unstable to me,' he croaked, loud enough for all to hear. 'Take my word for it, gentlemen. She'll be pooped in a following sea—if the weight of her engines don't take her to the bottom first.'

Captain Webster sniffed disparagingly. 'If that's the shape of things to come,' he growled, 'I thank a merciful Providence that I shan't live to see the day.' He rolled across to a chair in the front row, settled his fringe of whiskers upon the handle of his walking stick and subjected Robert to a steady unwinking stare. 'And what is more,' he mumbled at length, 'we have a fool for chairman.'

Robert glowered back at the old man, shifted uncomfortably, and his eyes counted the number of shareholders shuffling to their places. He leaned across to Albert. 'There are rather more than I expected.'

'I make it a baker's dozen,' said Albert. 'Small shareholders. No voting strength. What is your count, Tupman?'

Tupman had been calculating swiftly. 'Excluding Mr Callon, I give them three hundred and seventy votes, sir.'

'Not enough,' said Albert, satisfied. 'This rabble can hoot and bay all they want, we hold the whip hand.'

Robert nodded. 'Good. I'd better call the meeting to order.' He cleared his throat and banged with his gavel. The mutter of voices dropped to a murmur, then to an expectant silence.

'If I may have your attention, gentlemen? Perhaps I should begin by introducing myself and my colleague. I am Robert Onedin and, in the absence of your chairman, Mr James Onedin, I have been persuaded to take the chair.'

'By whom?' called a voice.

'Yes. Who elected you?' shouted another.

'I believe you have been supplied with a copy of the articles of association,' said Robert, smoothly. 'If you will turn to page three and consult paragraph four you will see that the chairman is elected by the board.'

'And can be removed by a vote of no confidence from the floor,' interjected Callon to a rumble of 'hear, hears'.

'Would you care to put it to the test, Mr Callon?' asked Albert.

'How many votes do you hold?' demanded the first voice, a rubicund gentleman with swollen red nose and ginger whiskers.

'Eighteen thousand, sir,' Albert told him.

'And I hold one thousand in my own name, and thirty thousand as proxy for my brother, James,' pronounced Robert, glaring at Red-nose.

'Are we to understand that the chairman intends to vote for himself?' The speaker was a thin, gaunt man with a goatee beard and the mournful expression of an undertaker's mute.

'No,' replied Robert. 'I shall step down and you shall take the chair. Or Mr Callon, if he so pleases.'

'And disenfranchise myself,' said Callon. 'No thank you.'

'Then perhaps,' said Robert, 'we can continue with the meeting? I was about to introduce our engineer and designer, Mr Albert Frazer. On the table before you you will see a model of Mr Frazer's brainchild, and I have no doubt that in due course you will wish to question Mr Frazer in some detail as to how he has been spending our money.'

He waited for the expected laugh, but was met instead with a stony silence. He hem-hemmed and shuffled his papers. 'This meeting was called at the behest of Mr Callon for the purpose of discussing the progress of the steamship. I think, before proceeding further, it only fair to remind

218

you that Mr Callon is himself an owner with heavy commitments in sail.'

'I am not one to stand in the way of progress,' responded Callon, unctuously. 'And as an earnest of my good faith I have invested no less than twenty-four thousand pounds in this venture.'

'Through nominees,' Albert interposed, quickly. He addressed the rest of the meeting. 'Gentlemen, ask yourselves why Mr Callon chose this back-door method of entering the company rather than buying shares openly like the rest of us.'

'I'll tell you why,' shouted Callon, coming to his feet and dominating his audience as he had dominated so many such meetings in the past. 'Because if James had once seen my name on the company register he would have had a shoal of his own nominees and you would all be in his pockets by now! And where is he? Where is this driving force? The inspiration behind that—that monstrosity?' He pointed a declamatory arm at the ship model. 'I'll tell you where he is—away on the high seas, looking after his own interests and leaving the company to flounder along as best it can! At a time when the company needs a firm hand upon the tiller, James Onedin takes himself off to the ends of the earth, leaving our affairs in the hands of incompetents! Incompetents, gentlemen! he roared. 'I say it again—incompetents!'

He sat down quickly to a tumult of stamping feet, waving agenda papers, calls of 'Shame!' and demands for resignation.

Robert, purple-faced, huffed and puffed and was about to rise angrily to his feet when Albert held out a restraining hand.

'Don't lose your temper, Robert—that is precisely his aim. It is votes that count, not insults.'

He held up his hands to silence the hubbub and smiled good-humouredly at the forest of waving arms. 'I congratulate Mr Callon on entertaining us with a fine example of emotional rhetoric; one which made up in fustian what it lacked in sensibility. And now, gentlemen, having dispensed with bombast, perhaps we can return to polemics. I am prepared to answer any questions on construction or design you may care to put forward. Yes— you, sir.'

A tall spare man of lean, intelligent features stood up. 'My name is Brandon. I, too, am an engineer, Mr Frazer.'

Albert immediately put him down as one of Callon's henchmen, no doubt primed with a list of prepared questions; he therefore leaned forward, put his fingertips together and gave the speaker the benefit of his full attention.

'I have examined the model with considerable interest,' Brandon commenced in the clear well-pitched voice of a reasonable man open to conviction. 'It certainly appears to be a radical departure from the accepted practice of shipbuilding as I understand it. First, sir, perhaps you would be good enough to explain to us why there is no provision for carrying sail in the event of a breakdown of the engine?'

The door at the back of the hall quietly opened and a stout fleshy man of wobbling jowls tiptoed into the room with exaggerated care, to take a place at the rear of the hall. Clasping plump hands across a cherry-red waistcoat, he creased his features into a simpering smile and settled himself to listen.

Robert nudged Tupman, who slid from his seat and unobtrusively made off to consult the newcomer.

'The function of an engine,' Albert was saying, 'is to dispense with anachronisms such as sails. If you will refer to our prospectus, which no doubt you consulted before risking your investments, you will read that the specifications called for a vessel designed to carry four and a half thousand tons of cargo, at a speed of thirteen knots, and with a range of six thousand miles. There is no mention of masts, spars, or canvas.'

'Nor is there any indication that it was built without such provision,' snapped Callon. 'Had I known I would not have invested so much as a penny piece. I consider it sharp practice, sir. Sharp practice.' He grinned around at the assembly. 'I think I'll ask for my money back.'

'If you wish to withdraw,' said Albert, coldly, 'I am sure we can accommodate you.'

'How?' demanded Callon. 'By going into liquidation and paying us off at a shilling in the pound? No thank you.'

'Then what is your interest?' asked Albert.

'To see that the business of this company is conducted on sound financial principles,' retorted Callon, to a chorus of 'hear, hears'.

'That's a charitable thought, coming from a sailing-ship man,' Albert commented, drily.

Brandon raised his voice in an effort to make himself heard against the clamour. 'You will not deny, Mr Frazer, that sails are an essential safety factor?'

'With one engine driving a single propeller, you may well be right. But with two engines driving two propellers the safety factor, Mr Brandon, will be of so high an order as to no longer justify the additional expense of sails and their manning.'

Albert's calm pronouncement seemed to silence them for a moment. They sat and stared at him in disbelief. Callon found his voice first. 'Two engines!' he spluttered. 'By God, there's arrogance for you! In one breath he tells us that sails are too expensive, in the next that he intends to install not one, but two of these coal-consuming monsters! With two sets of boilers to blow up, it doubles risk!'

Albert shook his head. 'The boilers will not blow up. Moreover, should one engine break down the other will take over, thus halving, not increasing, the risk.'

Brandon was frowning thoughtfully. 'Two propellers? Surely they will work in opposition to each other?'

Albert again shook his head. 'No. They will double the efficiency.'

'At double the cost!' shouted Callon.

Albert, safe on his own ground, smiled pityingly at Callon. 'You are thinking in terms of the old-fashioned slow-running, single-expansion engines. It is my intention to utilise Mr Elder's compound engines, each developing three thousand horsepower at a boiler pressure of sixty pounds to the square inch. Coal consumption is estimated at two pounds per horsepower per hour.'

Brandon scribbled quick calculations on the back of his agenda paper, while Callon seemed on the point of exploding like one of the boilers he had just condemned. Instead he gave vent to a paroxysm of coughing and took relief in a massive inhalation of snuff.

Tupman returned and whispered urgently to Robert: 'It's Mr Mitchell. Three thousand shares.'

'Mitchell!' questioned Robert. 'He has no right to attend.' He fished through his papers. 'I have it here—a copy of his agreement with James and Fogarty. Thank you, Tupman, I'll keep an eye on the rascal.'

Brandon completed his calculations and returned to the attack. 'Correct me if I am wrong, Mr Frazer, but my calculations translate your figures into a consumption of coal at the rate of two and a half tons per hour? Per engine?'

Albert nodded. 'That is a reasonable approximation.'

Callon regained his breath. 'Five tons an hour! With coal at sixteen shillings a ton, that works out at near a hundred pound a day! I can tell you where our money goes, gentlemen—up through that tin chimney and out in smoke! I demand to know why no provision has been made to take advantage of that free commodity, the wind!'

'Because we cannot calculate for the wind. The wind is a variable commodity, and can prove an expensive economy in the long run,' Albert told him, tartly.

'Bah!' snorted Callon, and, having made his point, sat down.

Brandon resumed: 'A marine engine capable of developing three thousand horsepower is unheard of, and certainly beyond my comprehension. I can only suggest that two such engines combined would be sufficient to shake the ship to pieces.' He held up a hand to wave away Albert's expostulations. 'No matter, no matter—perhaps we may now examine this quite realistic model in some detail. What is the purpose of that—athwartships structure, just forward of the funnel?'

'That, sir,' said Albert, irritably, 'is a bridge-walk. It is from here that the ship will be navigated. You will notice that from this position the officer of the watch will have a clear, all-round view of the horizon, unimpeded by masts and sails as is the case when navigating from the poop deck. Even you, sir, with your penchant for turning advantage into disadvantage must admit that anything which adds to the safety of a ship is an advance. Nor is it quite the innovation you pretend to imagine—I am sure it cannot have escaped your attention that bridge-walks, crossing from one sponson to another, are by no means uncommon on paddle steamers.'

'On the assumption that this—structure—is not washed overboard in the first heavy sea, how is it proposed to connect the steering wheel to the rudder?' pursued Brandon, ignoring Albert's comments.

'By a series of alternating iron rods and chains along the after deck.'

'Is it not an axiom in engineering that the strength of a chain lies in its weakest link? Will you tell us what happens to the ship should just one of those weak links snap?'

'It will be replaced, of course,' snapped Albert, growing weary of this constant bickering.

'Replaced?' sneered Callon. 'In a heavy sea? Have you ever served aboard a ship, young man?'

'No,' retorted Albert. 'And I beg leave to doubt you have ever designed an engine.'

In the resultant uproar Robert banged with his gavel and strove to make his voice heard. 'Gentlemen! Gentlemen! I beg of you! This is no way to conduct our business!'

The storm of voices abated to a growling murmur, a low assibilation of sound that whispered and muttered like the angry surge of a receding sea. 'Gentlemen,' Robert repeated. 'Mr Frazer has answered your questions with courtesy, patience and good humour. I must insist that you afford him that same courtesy. Are there any more questions?'

'I think I've heard enough,' said Callon. 'But I've one or two remarks that will bear utterance. I have no faith, gentlemen, no faith whatsoever in the design of this vessel in the form in which it has been presented to us. There was no mention in the prospectus of two monster engines of thousands of horsepower each, eating up coal at the rate of seven hundred pounds a week! Three thousand pounds a month! How much profit will be left at the end of six months' voyage? Precious little, if my arithmetic is anything to go by!'

'It isn't,' interrupted Albert, hotly. 'I have costed most carefully. You are calculating on the assumption that the ship will spend its entire life at sea. It won't. It will be in port, loading and discharging cargo for . . .'

'Fiddle-faddle,' snorted Callon. 'Kindly do not interrupt, young man, and have the decency to extend to me those courtesies demanded by the chairman for yourself. If I may continue, Mr Chairman?' he asked, bowing to Robert in mock humility. 'I am not against innovation, gentlemen, but I have been in business too long, and too successfully, to be hoodwinked by a catchpenny scheme such as this. I believe it may be possible to proceed with the construction given certain reasonable modifications.'

'Never!' cried Albert. 'Never! I will resign first!'

'That is your privilege, the exercise of which I, for one, would warmly welcome,' said Callon.

Robert plucked urgently at Albert's sleeve. 'You must not! You must stay and fight. Without you we are lost!'

'I am a reasonable man, putting forward no more than a reasonable request,' Callon continued. 'With masts and sails, one engine of somewhat less power and but one propeller, it might be possible to turn a profit. Handled with prudence and care, moving step by step, and by conducting the business on sound financial principles, it could very well prove a worthwhile proposition. But the time of decision is now, gentlemen, now—before that—that folly proceeds further!' He jabbed an outstretched arm at the model, while Albert sat tight-lipped and white with anger. 'Only the other day,' he stated, 'I was in conversation with Mr Alfred Holt. Mr Holt is building a new ship designed for the Far East trade. It will undoubtedly be one of the finest, most powerful steam vessels ever launched—with one propeller, three masts and a full set of sails, gentlemen!'

Callon sat down amid a roar of cheering and shouts of 'Resign! Resign!' cast at Robert and Albert.

Brandon sprang to his feet. 'I call for the resignation of the board, and nominate Mr Callon as chairman!'

'I second!' shouted Red-nose.

Robert pushed away his chair and, hauling himself up to full stature, faced a forest of waving papers and a tumult of shouts and stamping feet.

'Is it your wish to put it to the vote?' he demanded.

'Vote, vote, vote, vote!' they yelled.

'Very well,' said Robert. 'But before we take a count there is one gentleman who is present only on sufferance. Mr Mitchell—I must ask you to leave.'

Mitchell smiled and shook his head. 'No, sir.'

'Is it your intention to vote?'

'It is, sir.'

'Then I must rule you out of order,' said Robert, firmly. 'I have here a copy of an agreement bearing your signature, and stating quite clearly that your shares are to be held in abeyance until the return of the *Pandora* and *Medusa*.'

Mitchell flourished a lavender-coloured handkerchief and dabbed delicately at his lips. 'I, too, have a copy, Mr Chairman, and I can assure you that I am more than familiar with its contents. Particularly as it was written at Mr Onedin's insistence. Mr Onedin refused to accept my given word, an avowal which I found particularly offensive. However, the agreement is clear and succinct: I am not to sell, or otherwise dispose of my shares. But there is nothing

231

in that document which expressly forbids the exercise of my voting rights. I am here, sir, to exercise those rights.'

Robert saw the smirk of triumph on Callon's face and realised that they were beaten. Mustering his papers, he faced the angry calls with all the dignity at his command. 'I shall not put you to the trouble of voting, gentlemen. I shall resign. But I warn you—unless Mr Frazer remains on the board, your shares will soon not be worth the paper they are written on. And I might remind Mr Callon that a man who can be swayed in one direction today can, equally, be swayed in another, to-morrow.'

'Step down!' yelled someone.

Callon remained shrunk in thought, his lizard eyes unwinkingly focused upon some inner vision. There was a grey pallor to his features and his hands trembled as he leaned upon the head of his walking stick. He could feel his heart fluttering painfully and his chest constricting as though intent upon squeezing the breath from his lungs. He levered himself to his feet and opened his mouth to speak. A trickle of saliva drooled from the side of his mouth and the room disappeared into a vortex of roaring darkness.

He was still unconscious when they carried him home and laid him gently upon the large four-poster bed.

Robert and Albert stood looking down at their old adversary while Dr Merrydew, hastily summoned, completed his examination.

'A seizure,' he pronounced. 'I warned him, time and time again. But he's a stubborn man. He would not listen . . .'

Callon opened one eye. 'I'm done for,' he whispered. 'Done for.' A tear trickled down his face.

'Lie still,' commanded Merrydew. 'Or you will be.'

'Albert.' The old man's breath sighed in his throat. 'Build your ship. Two engines. Too ambitious. Not practical. Cost too great for competition. Wait. Profits first. Your time will come.' His hand reached out to clutch and grip Albert's wrist. 'One engine only. Promise.'

Albert hesitated. The grip tightened and one side of Callon's face twisted in the grimace of a grin. 'Promise, or I'll outvote ye, yet.'

'I promise,' said Albert.

One eye remained open, staring sightlessly in the stricture of paralysis. The other closed as though in a slow deliberate wink as the mind sank towards the abyss of unconsciousness. His tongue strove to push forward half-formed sentences.

'Robert.'

'I am here,' said Robert, bending low to catch the thickly mumbled speech.

'You are a very good chairman, my boy. Very good.'

'Thank you,' said Robert, gratefully, and hoping the others could hear.

'Do not resign. Keep control. Guide company.' The eye opened again. 'See to it that he keeps his word.'

'I will,' Robert promised, firmly.

'Good,' said Callon, satisfied. His breath wheezed and for a moment Robert had the strangest feeling that Callon was laughing. Then he slid away into a shallow sleep, one Cyclopean eye remaining open to stare, glazed and sightless, at the ceiling.

They tiptoed away, leaving him to Merrydew and his grey-haired manservant, John.

Albert took a hansom, but Robert,

needing time to pick and rummage over the day's events, decided to walk. Callon spoke uncommon good sense, he mused, ignoring the outstretched hand of a bedraggled match-seller, and skirting a vociferous group of argumentative maidservants. Yes, a man on his death-bed, with the immediate prospect of meeting his Maker, could not help but speak the truth. 'You will make a fine chairman,' Callon had said, and Robert was forced, in all humility, to agree with the asseveration; all things considered, whichever way one looked at it, he had handled that meeting with firmness, tact and diplomacy; the hallmark of a first-class chairman, there was no denying it. He puffed out his chest, held back his head and, with commanding eyes, surveyed a rabble of urchins, sweeping them aside with flourishes of his stick when they rushed forward to surround him, cartwheeling and screeching and begging for coppers. He strode on purposefully, ignoring their jeers of 'Skinflint', and an ill-aimed clod of horse-manure which missed his hat by a yard.

'Keep control of the company,' Callon had begged with his dying breath. Robert's heart warmed to the man. He had proved a worthy adversary: honest, open, forthright; stating his opinions without fear or favour; and, what is more, he spoke uncommon good sense. 'Build the ship with sails and one engine.' Sound advice, sound advice indeed. Particularly from a man of Mr Callon's business acumen. Not the sort of man to saddle himself with a white elephant; which, in Robert's considered opinion, was exactly what Albert's monstrous ship would prove to be, unless one applied the brake of commonsense to the juggernaut of ambition. Robert rather liked the phrase and repeated it to himself: perhaps he could incorporate it in his opening speech at the next meeting. Yes, indeed, he would call one as soon as possible. There, he would make his position clear, take a stand and, with James's proxy votes in his pocket, brook no interference from Albert or anyone else, but carry out Callon's wishes to the letter.

Sonorous phrases ringing in his mind, he rounded the corner to discover a pink-faced Sarah and a purple-visaged Mrs Arkwright screeching at each other like fish-wives.

'There you are!' exclaimed Sarah,

standing in the shop doorway, arms akimbo.

'There he is!' squawked Mrs Arkwright, wattles shaking in anger. 'The scoundrel! Thief! Rogue! Liar and cheat!'

'What—?' Robert began, the dominant chairman fleeing hot-foot for sanctuary.

'My husband will deal with you, madam!' said Sarah, nodding her head vehemently, clasping her hands in front, and pulling back her shoulders.

'I am not in the habit of brawling in the street!' shrieked Mrs Arkwright, taking an imperious step toward the shop.

Sarah stood her ground. 'I am not in the habit of brawling anywhere,' she retorted, waiting for Robert's approach.

Robert stared from one to the other. 'I don't understand—?'

'Don't understand? Don't understand!' Mrs Arkwright waved her parasol imploringly to heaven. 'He don't understand!' she pleaded. 'D'ye deny, ye villain, that you connived with that scheming minx to rob me of me household silver? Deny it, if you dare, ye scoundrel!'

'Silver? What silver?' asked Robert, bemused.

'My best silver! Heirlooms, handed down from my late father. The poor man will turn in his grave! I shall swear out an information and prosecute to the fullest extent of the law unless every piece is returned!'

'It would seem, madam,' said Robert, stiffly, 'that you have taken leave of your senses. I have no knowledge of your confounded silverware, and have no wish to be enlightened further.'

'No wish to be enlightened further!' repeated the enraged woman. 'That I can well believe! Bah, sir! Bah! I suppose you will next deny that you were having a clandestine affair with that ungrateful wretch!'

'I do indeed!' hooted Robert, his heart suddenly churning into his mouth. 'How dare you, madam! How dare you utter such a calumny! You will hear from my solicitors, by heaven, unless you retract immediately! My relationship with your Miss Simmonds was entirely above reproach! A straightforward business relationship, nothing else.' He spared a quick glance at Sarah to assess the effect of his words. To his relief she was nodding approval. He sucked in a breath and spoke more calmly. 'If you have sustained a loss due to the depredations of one of your staff, I suggest you lodge a complaint with the proper authorities, and not waste your time by brow-beating my wife. I will not tolerate it, madam. I will not tolerate it.'

Mrs Arkwright seemed suddenly deflated. 'But what am I to do?' she asked. 'What am I to do? The wretched creature—after all I have done for her—ran off, without so much as a by-your-leave—taking a chest of silver with her. And I don't know where she is,' she wailed. 'I don't know where she is.'

'I can enlighten you there,' said Robert, cruelly. 'She is on her way to La Rochelle, and I doubt very much that you will ever see her or your precious silver again. And now I must bid you good-day. I have business to attend to. Come, Sarah, my dear.'

He took Sarah's arm and guided her triumphantly inside, leaving Mrs Arkwright to clamber into the waiting carriage and return home to bewail her loss in private.

CHAPTER 12

A SKY the colour of burnt parchment hung over a copper sea. To the east the horizon was a furnace glow as though distant hidden fires had set the world alight. A school of flying fish traced quickly erased pencil marks across plains of water, and then disappeared with a series of plops and splashes into an indigo sea. Far to the west the last few stars hung like jewels, only to wink and die in the wash of a salmon dawn as the giant red disc of the sun heaved itself above the horizon. Its oven-heat drove the cool night breeze before it, to shiver and fill the *Medusa*'s bleached white sails.

Passarees boomed outboard thirty feet at the fore, and with a full complement of stunsails and staysails, the *Medusa* carried every stitch of canvas she could bear. Even so, were it not for the pucker of water at her bows and the chuckling run beneath her stern, she would appear to be lost and motionless amidst a waste of sky and water.

They had run south and west until they

had sighted the bulging coast of Brazil then, picking up the Trades, had run south and east to dip into the Roaring Forties, where they had foamed along, reeling off the knots, decks awash, every sail bellied in the wind, and sea spume torn from the tops of white horses, rising like geysers. Islands of whales had spurted and spouted, and the wild sea birds had planed the waves, calling plaintive liturgies to an unheeding world of roaring winds and bitter seas.

Then, rounding the Cape of Good Hope, they had entered the vastness of the Indian Ocean and set their course north and east, with a warm friendly wind coming in over the quarter and bowling them along at a steady twelve knots.

Now they were ninety days out and never once had they caught sight of another sail, and the wind had shifted to blow fitfully from the east, sometimes falling away to leave them becalmed on an ocean of molten gold. It also brought a sticky humidity and a warm sickly smell as of rotting vegetation.

'We are in the lee of the land,' James had told them, poring over his charts.

There was no need to impress upon the masthead look-outs the importance of keeping their eyes peeled, for every man aboard had the scent of land in his nostrils and thirsted for a sight of land as an animal, crossing a desert, will thirst for water.

The sea mist hung low in swirling veils. Mr Llewellyn struck four bells and idly watched the day workers turning to with pots of paint and varnish, while the job watch lethargically prepared to wash down the decks.

A faint, uncertain 'Halloo' from the lookout brought all heads up in a questing search. Except for the monotonous lap of water and the steady creak of rigging, the ship was silent. Then, borne across the wrinkled surface of the sea, came a strange, ghostly tinkling. They stood and listened, staring blankly, heads cocked, ears straining.

The sound rose and fell, rippled and strummed, distorted by distance.

It was Llewellyn who first identified the notes. 'By damn!' he blurted. 'It's a bloody piano!' and ran below to tell James.

The mystery was resolved when the sea mist cleared to reveal, far to the east, the topsails of a ship lying just beyond the horizon.

Anne, eyes screwed against the glare of sea and sun, was listening intently. 'I think it is a hymn tune.' She began to sing softly:

'Lead us, heavenly Father, lead us,
O'er the world's tempestuous sea;
Guard us, guide us, keep us, feed us,
For we have no help but thee.'

James, squinting through the telescope, paused to wipe away perspiration trickling into his eyes. He tried again, screwing his features into a grimace of ferocious concentration. Then he passed the telescope to Anne.

'I think, I think we've caught her.'

Armstrong's shark-head grinned down from his perch high on the mizzen crosstrees. 'It's her, right enough,' he called. 'Dammee if it isn't the *Pandora*. Becalmed and all a-droop like a lady's petticoats, begging your pardon, ma'am.'

The *Medusa* altered course and ghosted along with barely a whisper of breeze. By noon they could see the *Pandora* quite clearly, canvas flapping idly as she rolled sluggishly in the long, slow ocean swell.

'By four o'clock in the afternoon watch,'

Anne wrote in her journal, 'we were standing off about a mile distant, which gave us a most excellent view of the *Pandora*, and we were all agreed that she did indeed faithfully represent Mr Coleridge's poetic image of "a painted ship on a painted sea". The air was now so still we could scarce breathe and our sails were hard put to draw. James therefore signalled the *Pandora* that we should be paying her a visit, and ordered a boat over the side, leaving Mr Armstrong in charge of the ship.

'In honour of the occasion I had put on a new linen suit, the making of which had pleasantly occupied my time during the latter part of the voyage. My features, of course, are disgracefully brown, but I do so enjoy the fresh sea airs and my little promenades on deck, that I feel it a price well worth the paying.

'On reaching the *Pandora* we received a rousing cheer from the crew, and I was hoisted aboard in a chair while James made his way up a rope ladder.

'Dear Emma greeted me most effusively, positively casting herself into my embrace and laughing and crying at one and the same time. Then she quickly hurried me below to the seclusion and comfort of their state-room, James and Daniel remaining to exchange civilities above.'

Pausing to chew at her pen, Anne's eyes wandered to the open stern windows and the green island of Krakatao slowly drifting past, as the *Medusa* led the way through the Sunda Straits. A misshapen saucer of cloud overhung the island's peak. Native fishing villages, half-buried in jungle, straggled along the shore-line. Outrigger canoes and proas loaded with coconuts and fresh fruit bobbed in the ships' wash, and their owners' cries of 'Barter! Barter!' hung in the air long after the ships had passed.

She tore away her gaze and returned to her task. 'Emma was attired in a pleasing costume of muslin and organdie, and a wide-brimmed straw hat with a net veil to protect her complexion from the sun. (James later remarked that she looked more like a bee-keeper than a captain's wife!)

'We took tea in her quarters (the last word in luxury!) and indulged ourselves in the fripperies of female conversation, from which I learned that the poor child had been dreadfully seasick at first, receiving but scant sympathy from Daniel. Later she recovered, but it would seem the experience has left its mark, for she appears to have spent most of the voyage moping in her room, reading, sewing a little, and dabbling in water colours. (She showed me one or two. They are quite pretty, but their subject matter is entirely confined to English countryside scenes painted from memory. I am afraid the unhappy child suffers dreadfully from homesickness.)

'It is also evident that she has evinced not the slightest interest in shipboard life and, even now, can barely distinguish one mast from another.

'Poor Emma. Nothing in her education can have prepared her for the rigours of a long sea passage. She also seems to combine romantical and fanciful notions with a woeful ignorance of the world which the door of marriage opened for her. There is also, I regret to say, a noticeable coolness between her and Daniel. I do hope and pray that it does not lead to an estrangement!

'Later we had a quite excellent dinner of

chicken and yams—a sort of sweet potato—followed by delicious fruit and glasses of coconut milk. (Obtained when Daniel put into Moni Island, about 200m south of here, for fresh water and a few stores.)

'Afterwards, Emma entertained us at the piano with a few pieces from her considerable repertoire. She is a quite accomplished pianist and has the gift of a melodious singing voice. Daniel, who has a pleasing baritone, sang a duet with her, and we all joined in a quartette to the rousing tune of "The Lily-white Boys", finally rounding off the evening with the "Bay of Biscay-o". Emma sang as lustily as the rest, and we finished panting and laughing and quite exhausted.

'But all good things must come to an end, and when the Mate, Mr Pritchard, knocked to tell Daniel that the wind was backing and freshening, it was time to take our leave. James and Daniel had agreed that our respective positions were a few miles off the westernmost tip of Java, and James suggested that we proceed to our destination in convoy (in company, he said tactfully, for Emma's benefit), a proposition with which Daniel heartily concurred. And not without reason! For it is widely held that the waters of the South China Seas, which we are about to enter, are infested with pirates of most barbarous aspect and ferocious demeanour. James had already had our brass cannons run out, and the crew are well practised in their use. But is is my earnest wish that we are not forced to use them. If only for poor Emma's sake! I am sure the poor child would never survive the experience of being attacked!

'I have but one footnote to add before closing my journal for the day. I believe I am once more with child! ! ! I shall seek an opportunity to break the news gently to James—for he does worry so!'

She laid aside her pen, closed the leather-bound book, and remained for long moments staring dreamily into the future. Then, pulling herself together, she hurried on to deck.

The *Pandora*, under topsails and courses, followed in line astern as the ships glided between towering cliffs of jungle. Monkeys chattered and howled, and an explosion of birds rose like multi-coloured rockets. The deep ocean blue was giving way to a pale sea-green wash.

James put an arm about her shoulders. 'Sumatra to your left, Java to your right. And the China Seas, right ahead.'

CHAPTER 13

BAINES had earned himself the soubriquet of 'Lucky'. For fortune had indeed seemed to favour him.

After parting company with the *Medusa* they drove south under blue skies and with a stiff quartering breeze and six days out made their first landfall, bringing up the island of Madeira fine on the port bow. Five days later they sighted the Cape Verdes and, logging a steady 280 miles a day, crossed the Line fifteen days out from Liverpool.

The weather held, and they sailed through the Doldrums as though Baines had brought along a private bag of wind of his own.

They were halcyon days with the *Pampero* reeling off the knots and never once carrying away so much as a rope yarn. She surged along, a white ship in an ocean of blue, tar bubbling in the seams of snow-white decks, and towers of canvas reaching to the sky.

'We'll pay for it, rounding the 'orn,' the

older hands forecast, crossing their fingers superstitiously. 'We'll be in the teeth of a westerly wi' snow and ice and seas like mountains. There'll be broken bones afore this voyage is over. She's a widow-maker, is the 'orn, a widow-maker.'

One of the younger hands nodded confidently toward the magician in brass-bound uniform of bleached blue, slowly pacing the poop. 'Old Scratch'll get us through,' he said.

The sailmaker looked up from his task of cutting out a new staysail, growled deep in his chest and waved his razor-sharp knife at the speaker. 'Spit it out, bucko. Spit out that word. Mention the Devil and he'll come for his own—and take the rest of us with him.'

The sailor blanched, spat quickly and put a hand over his mouth to stop the Devil flying back in. 'I meant Lucky,' he said, apologetically. 'Didn't mean no offence. What I'm saying is we got a lucky ship wi' a lucky master.'

The sailmaker nodded approval. 'Lucky Baines,' he said. 'Let's hope his luck holds,' and he, too, spat to spare the Devil.

'Amen,' answered the sailor, fervently.

Baines's luck did hold. South of the Falklands the weather broke at last. Banks of low cloud scudded across the horizon and the sea showed its teeth in foaming white breakers. A westerly gale howled out of the desolation of Tierra del Fuego and laid the *Pampero* over until she was running with her port bulwarks under. Baines brought her round and ran before the wind until he calculated they were well clear of Staten Island. Then he turned south, stood out to sea to give himself plenty of elbow room, and prayed that the wind would abate.

His prayers must have been answered for the wind shifted and backed. With the characteristic changeability of weather off the Horn, visibility cleared and the wind blew strongly from the east. The *Pampero* curtsied as though in acknowledgement.

They had stretched lifelines along the main deck, overhauled the gear aloft, and snugged down to lower topsails. It was now or never. Baines sucked in a deep breath and gave the order: 'All she can bear, Mr Tranter,' he told the first mate.

They shook out lower courses and upper topsails and fled before the wind. Two days later they brought up the Horn, a lumbering mass of black rock jutting out of the sea; forbidding, wild and forlorn; the end of the world sheered off as though with a knife.

Its name was a misnomer, being neither cape nor horn, but a conical island gouged with ice-filled gullies; but its reputation was none the less fearsome; for here the two mightiest oceans in the world converged in a seething maelstrom of water, with sixty-foot waves, and troughs between deep enough to engulf a ship. Beyond lay nothing but a freezing hell of ice and snow.

The wind increased in power, seas roared along the weather rail, racing and foaming along the deck. The *Pampero* strained and panted in her urgency to outrun the following cliffs of green water threatening to overtake and drag her down by the stern.

It was winter and the sun rose at nine to hang like a ball of fire over the bitter landscape, then set at three to plunge the world into raging darkness.

At eight bells they hove the log, one of the seamen holding the reel above his head while the second mate guided the log line and float over the after rail. Mr Tranter watched the white rag mark flash over the rail, checked the time from the second hand of his watch, and called: 'Stop!'

The second mate held the line on the rail and looked for the nearest mark. 'Fifteen knots!' It seemed incredible. The *Pampero* was rounding the Horn at a speed which would not have disgraced a tea clipper.

Four days later she entered the Pacific and headed north for Valparaiso.

The long, narrow, barren coast of Chile stretched for two and a half thousand miles from the Horn to the borders of Peru, with the principal port of Valparaiso approximately in the middle. Cut off from the rest of the South American continent by the enormous barrier of the Andes, parched by desert, shaken by earth tremors, it had but one attraction: seemingly inexhaustible supplies of copper, nitrate and guano, which drew the ships of every trading nation in the world like a magnet. In return they brought coal and the trappings of civilisation. But from the inaccessible mountains of the south, riven by fiords and glaciers, to the rainless, fiery Atacama

Desert in the north, it truly earned its title of the hell coast.

Sixty-two days out from Liverpool, not a record, but a markedly fast passage, the *Pampero* dropped anchor in Valparaiso Bay. The town huddled beneath steep cliffs, up which writhed dusty paths with occasional rickety flights of wooden steps leading to the infamous barrios of the red-light district. Over all brooded the snow-capped peak of Aconcagua, towering even above the mighty peaks of the Andes.

Baines had himself rowed ashore to inquire of the consul as to the disposal of his cargo and, more important, the prospects of picking up another.

The consul was a gloomy, dyspeptic man with an abiding hatred of all things pertaining to the sea, and seamen in particular. He forecast a wait of at least four months in Valparaiso and advised Baines to head north the moment he had completed discharging and scout the lesser ports. They sat on the terrace overlooking the harbour, sipping anisado and idly counting the ships moored in the bay.

There were dozens of vessels, barques and barquentines, brigs and Yankee whalers; most lay high out of the water, weed and barnacles clinging to their sides, as they waited through long hot, interminable weeks for their cargoes. There were no railways, everything being transported from the burning interior by burro and pack mule. The ships were hungry, and the trek from the copper mines was long and arduous, even for the hardy burros. So the ships waited and waited while their crews drank themselves into insensibility ashore on cheap aguadiente, the so-called teeth-melter, until their pay ran out. Then they deserted in droves, some to ship in the Chilean navy, some to become beggars, some—the more fortunate—to become crimps, boarding-house keepers, or managers of cantinas.

Baines noticed that lighters were beginning to cluster around the *Pampero* and the first of her cargo of pianos, glassware, cottons and linen was being slung over the side from the cock-billed yardarms, while the voices of the crew toiling at the hand-windlass rolled across the harbour:

'Ye've robbed many a whaler,
And ye've poxed many a sailor,

But ye'll never roll down Lime Street
   any more.
Maggie May, Maggie May . . .'

He took his leave of the consul and made his way back to the quay along the Calle San Martino, which belied its name by being the site of bordels, drinking dives and dance halls. Passing a fandango house with its shattering clack of castanets and the strumming of guitars, he pondered over one of the oddities of command. Given more authority than a magistrate, or even a wigged judge, he was answerable to no one but himself. He was his own master; and yet, a few short months ago he would not have hesitated, but pushed open the doors, picked one of the dancers in high-heeled shoes and flouncy skirts, and woken in the morning with a head as thick as a plank and not a penny to his name. Authority changed things. A man could not maintain discipline unless he first practised upon himself.

Thus musing he trudged along the dusty street, absently whisking away the ever-present flies buzzing in clouds to settle on eyes and lips, when a whining voice broke into his thoughts with a plea of: 'A centavo,

Mr Captain, sir. A centavo for a British seaman down on his luck.'

Baines glanced at the beggar, a typical ragamuffin of a beachcomber, a gaunt tatterdemalion of untrimmed beard, lice-infested hair and bare, dirt-encrusted feet, and was about to pass on; but something in the man's accent gave him cause to pause a moment in his stride.

'You're a Liverpool lad, aren't you?'

'Yes, sir, Captain, sir. From the port of Liverpool.'

'And a deserter, I'll be bound.'

'I was shanghaied, sir, and treated hard, cruel hard. Beat black and blue. I'm no sailor, sir, I was a clerk in a shipping office.'

'You were crimped,' said Baines, putting his hand into his pocket and fishing out a peso. It was an old story; the days of the press gangs were long over, but crimps had taken their place and were making a fortune. This scarecrow should have known better. If you drank in a seaman's pub what else could you expect but to wake up aboard some blubber boat, with a sore head and a bucko mate.

'No sir. It was all a mistake. I was employed by the house of Callon, sir, which you may well know if you ship from the Pool? It was arranged, sir. A Mr Tupman. But he jumped overboard and swam ashore.' He fixed his eyes greedily upon the peso. Baines flipped it in the air.

'Tupman, did you say?'

'Yes, sir. If you could spare a coin?'

'Arranged, you said. By whom?'

'Mr Callon, sir.'

'What's your name, my lad?'

'Blenkinsop, sir. I was inveigled, sir, by a villain named Drummond.'

'Friend of yours?'

'A fellow clerk, sir. But a villain, a villain of the deepest dye.'

Baines rubbed his chin. 'One of Callon's creatures?'

'Yes, sir. If ever I return home I'll give him such a drubbing, by God, I will.'

'You want to go home?'

'Oh, yes, sir, indeed, I do, sir. I'll do anything, sir. Anything.'

Baines pointed out across the bay. 'That's the *Pampero*. An Onedin ship. If you've a mind for it I'll sign you as galley swab.'

Tears made runnels down Blenkinsop's face. 'Thank you, sir. Oh, thank you, sir.

You'll not regret your generosity, I promise.'

'Very well,' said Baines. 'Follow me to the quay. Once aboard, you'll dump those rags over the side, scrape off your whiskers and scrub yourself clean. I want no lice aboard my ship. D'ye understand?'

'Aye, sir,' said Blenkinsop gratefully, and fell into step behind his new master.

In fourteen days they had off-loaded their cargo, weighed anchor, and thankfully headed out to sea, clear of the crowded harbour with its stench of decaying fish, guano and fertiliser.

They crept north, hugging the coast, peering in at the shipping waiting in the ports. They passed Coquimbo, Huasco, Caldera and Taltal. Antofagasta and Iquique. Their search took them past guano islands covered to a depth of sixty to a couple of hundred feet in rich bird droppings, Chinese coolies toiling in a roasting hell of choking yellow dust, while the ships stood off loading from lighters.

Baines shook his head and pressed on. Arica tempted him; there were no more than half a dozen full-rigged ships lying at their moorings. But they also seemed to be lying idle. He decided to try one more port, Ilo, a hundred miles to the north.

The days were unbearably hot, with the scorching wind from the inferno of the thousand-mile-long Atacama Desert tormenting their skins and drying the very moisture in their eyes. All suffered from raging, unquenchable thirsts, and their ration of a gallon of fresh water a day seemed to do little but bring on attacks of stomach cramps.

The *Pampero* stood off Ilo and Baines clapped the telescope to his eye. The harbour was deserted but for a couple of down-at-heel brigs flying the Peruvian flag. He changed the focus and squinted across at the raw desert shimmering in the heat haze. He paused and then looked more intently. Far away, swimming toward him, was a long black line, like a trail of ants. Baines concentrated his vision and the leading dark smudges resolved themselves into the shapes of mules and llamas, each laden with a double-sided pack. The tail of the pack train disappeared in the reflected glare of the sun. He swung his telescope, and to north and south were other trains, all converging upon the port.

He brought the *Pampero* round, and two hours later they dropped anchor in eight fathoms of water.

'First come, first served,' said Baines, and hurried ashore with a fat bribe for the mining agent.

Señor Pasco was a dapper smiling man who stroked his waxed moustache and accepted the gift and the news with equal aplomb. His office, like the rest of the town, was covered in a film of gritty dust blown in from the desert. The shutters were wide open and glass an unheard-of luxury, but the walls were of thick adobe and the interior comparatively cool.

They sat sipping light Chilean wine, and Señor Pasco stopped tantalising his moustache long enough to spread his hands affably. Certainly Capitan Beans could have the entire shipment. There was, of course, the matter of Señor Pasco's small commission to be considered. A peso a load, perhaps? For he was a poor man; but even the poor must eat.

Capitan Beans answered in fluent Spanish that he was honoured by Señor

Pasco's courtesy in bringing this little matter to his attention, but thought that twenty-five centavos would be more acceptable to his principal, Señor Onedin, who was known to be a hard and tyrannical master.

Señor Pasco sympathised, remarked that as a hidalgo he was unused to haggling and would, therefore, be pleased to accept fifty centavos.

Capitan Beans suggested forty centavos and a cask of rum.

Señor Pasco, in view of his great friendship for Capitan Beans, would be delighted to accept with the addition of an English clock.

Baines, who had sailed the coast many times, had come prepared. At the completion of loading he would make a present to his good friend Señor Pasco of a clock which said 'Cuckoo' every quarter of an hour.

Baines rather enjoyed bargaining in Spanish. He found it a language of politeness and pleasantries; but once a bargain was struck, it would be kept. It would be kept, of course, because if Señor Pasco should renegue it was understood that Baines would bring his crew ashore, personally break Señor Pasco's head and shake the town about his ears.

But such possibilities were not discussed between gentlemen, so they shook hands and settled down to serious drinking, Baines contributing a bottle of rum and Señor Pasco a sausage-shaped 'treepa' of aguadiente.

The windows of the office overlooked the dusty treeless plaza, and the few wooden and adobe shacks which constituted the town. Baines and Señor Pasco drank reflectively, chewed a few dried figs, and munched 'tacos' and hot peppered beans, until the sun dipped below the horizon and the night turned purple, and a jingle of harness heralded the approach of the leaders of the pack train.

They were a pitiful sight, eyes rolling in their heads, foam flecking their lips, sides heaving, legs trembling; even as Baines watched, one of the mules moaned, its legs buckled and it lay down with neck outstretched and tongue lolling in the dust of the square.

One of the drovers, a short, stunted, bow-legged man with baggy trousers, shaggy alpaca jacket and wide-brimmed hat, walked up to the animal, gave it an experimental kick, then drawing his long, razor-sharp *cuchillo* from its sheath, matter-of-factly slit its throat. He removed the packs and harness and unhurriedly set about butchering the carcass.

It was small reward, thought Baines, for humping a hundredweight or so of nitrate across 250 miles of waterless desert. It was a hard trade they were engaged in, sparing neither man nor beast. But if the world wanted minerals, then some must dig and others carry.

He finally took his leave from his good friend Señor Pasco and weaved unsteadily back to the ship.

It took 500 pack animals, six lighters, thirty-six *lancheros* and the crew working watch and watch about, forty-two days to load the *Pampero* with 1,200 tons of copper and saltpetre.

On the last day Baines took Mr Tranter ashore with him as an especial mark of esteem. Together they paid their respects to Señor Pasco, and Baines formally handed over the promised cuckoo clock while the effusive Señor Pasco poured tumblers of red wine.

With the clock whirring and hiccuping from its new perch on the wall, they sat watching the *Pampero* and waiting for the ceremony of hoisting the last bag aboard. It had been agreed that Blenkinsop, as the newest hand, would have the privilege of being hauled up with it. At this point Mr Pardon, the second mate, would race along the deck igniting a line of rockets, the crew would give three hearty cheers and drink the health of the ship, the captain, the owner, and anyone else who took their fancy, in good red rum. The native *lancheros* would be liberally supplied with liquor. The port's one and only fandango house had already opened its doors, dusted off its piano and enrolled the services of a dozen *mestizas*, plump, button-eyed girls with suet-dumpling faces and the duck-like walk of those used to carrying heavy burdens on their shoulders.

The *Pampero* was framed in the window like an oil painting. The sky was a strange lemon colour giving the oily swell of the sea beyond the harbour a curious sulphurous-yellow appearance. The air was suddenly still, and the familiar sounds of the town seemed to filter through to the ears as though through cotton wool.

The last bag was being hoisted aboard with Blenkinsop standing proudly atop. He should have been waving the house flag and calling for three cheers, but instead he dropped the flag, gaped open his mouth and gesticulated wildly. The seamen were also behaving strangely, running to the rails and staring down over the shipside.

Tranter suddenly put down his glass and came to his feet.

'My God!' he said. 'She's sinking!'

It wasn't possible! But the *Pampero* indeed appeared to be slowly settling to the bottom. She began to list to port; the cock-billed yard from which Blenkinsop was suspended snapped and fell to the deck in a tumble of rigging. The masts strained, and one of the foremast's shrouds parted with a 'twang'. Baines thought he saw Blenkinsop scrambling to his feet from the wreckage of the yard-arm, then he saw one of the brigs slither down the side of the mole, shedding spars and masts to settle on the mud. Mud! Baines pointed a shaking arm. 'It's the sea!' he croaked hoarsely, not believing his own words. 'It's the sea! The sea's going back!'

It was true. The waters of the harbour were receding, flowing back into the ocean. Inshore, lighters had grounded, their *lancheros* jumping over the side to flounder waist deep through stinking mud to the safety of the shore.

Then the sea returned.

It gathered itself in an enormous twenty-foot-high wave and roared into the harbour, carrying everything before it. The *Pampero* rose high and her starboard anchor cable snapped like cotton; the brig broke into matchwood; the *lancheros* disappeared in a welter of wild water; three of the *Pampero*'s lighters rode the top of the tidal wave like surf-boats, were carried high in the air and smashed into the town like projectiles. One landed in the plaza, another tore through a row of houses, the third ploughed into the fandango house carrying the loitering dance-hall girls before it in a mass of bloody pulp.

The wave reached the office, swirled about their feet, and then receded again. Out in the bay the *Pampero* was bucking frenziedly at its remaining cable, shaking and dragging its anchor across the sea bed.

The glasses began a crazy tinkling dance upon the table, the ground beneath their feet vibrated rapidly.

'*El tremblor*,' whispered Señor Pasco, and, crossing himself, began to pray fervently. '*El tremblor! Ah, por Dios, por Dios, por Dios . . .*'

Baines stood, shaking from head to foot, eyes wide, terror gripping him in a paralysis of shock. '*El terremoto!*' he managed at last. 'By God, it's an earthquake! Run, man, run! Run for your life!'

They took to their heels and raced through the shattered town, the earth trembling beneath their feet, while the terrified inhabitants scurried from no-where to nowhere like panic-stricken ants.

At the water's edge they found a native canoe thrown high on the beach. They manhandled it down, pushed it out, seized a couple of pieces of driftwood and paddled furiously for the ship. The sea boiled, spinning eddies and whirlpools and creating miniature tide races. Lengths of broken timber, an upturned boat, a tangle of sail and rigging swirled about them threatening to capsize their clumsy craft.

The sky turned brown, blotting out the

sun and casting an eerie malevolent darkness over the bay. The sea withdrew, plunged forward again, spouting enormous geysers and exploding bubbles of poisonous sulphur fumes.

Somehow they reached the ship, crashing into the side and overturning their unstable craft. Someone on deck threw down lifelines and they scrambled aboard, breathless and bleeding and with the fear of death in their eyes.

'Make sail! Make sail!' Baines roared, the deck heaving beneath his feet as the *Pampero* lurched and leaped crazily. 'Slip the cable!' he bellowed. 'Slip the cable!'

The topsails flapped, the spanker rattled up, the jib boomed and thrashed, while the carpenter raced forward with his mawl to aim panic-stricken blows at the shackle pin.

A wind, a wind, prayed Baines. Oh, God, send us a wind.

The wind came, unlike any wind he had ever known. At first it rose vertically over the town in a whirling tempest of dust and sand, carrying with it the debris of the shattered town. Roofs and shutters, splintered timbers and clay tiles rose and spun in a mad dance. Then, as the shackle pin finally shot out and the straining cable tore through the hawse pipe, a storm of choking yellow wind roared across the harbour.

The main upper and lower topsails burst under the strain, the jib sheets parted and the jib blew out in tatters. The fore lower topsail yard-arm carried away taking two of the crew with it. The *Pampero* pointed her head to the open sea and, rolling insanely, yawing wildly, she slipped and slithered rather than sailed out into a confusion of wild water and leaping seas.

Their stunned senses became aware of a long deep rumbling and Baines, turning his head to glance back, stood riveted at the sight of what was once the port of Ilo. The harbour was a boiling cauldron, the mole had disappeared, the entire beach was sliding forward into the sea taking with it the remains of the few adobe houses. He could pick out some of the surviving inhabitants, running haphazardly this way and that as though an ant heap had been stirred up. Even as he watched, a fissure opened across the plaza and the sea spurted through, blowing paving stones high in the air. The steep cliffs to the south split and

271

cracked and fell upon the town, pushing all before them in an avalanche of sand and boulders. Fires began to glow redly then, igniting the dry timbers, burst into tornadoes of searing yellow flames. He saw Señor Pasco's office slowly crumble into a heap of rubble, then the earth opened its jaws, swallowed and closed.

He turned away to a renewed volume of shouting from the crew. Ahead of them, stretching from horizon to horizon, rolled a smooth mountain of water, the glassy smoothness of its surface mottled and stained with streaks of leprous colour. It stood ninety feet high from trough to crest and moved with the speed of an express train. Out of the corner of his eye Baines saw the break of foam beginning to ripple along its apex as the tidal wave, reaching the shallows, began to gather itself into a curling overwhelming mass. The *Pampero*'s bows lifted, rose higher and higher, until she seemed to stand on end. The crest was hurtling toward them, breaking with a sound like thunder. For dizzying seconds, as they clung to rails and lines, the ship seemed to hang in space, with the impetus of the wave carrying them remorselessly shore-wards. Then the bows dipped, the stern lifted and the *Pampero* slid down the other side.

Astern of them the wave burst into a welter of white water, roared across the harbour and swept inland, engulfing the remains of the broken town.

Then it receded to leave nothing but a curved shingle-strewn beach of mud and rock, with here and there the forlorn reminder of a headstone torn from the cemetery, embedded in a piece of adobe wall.

Of the port of Ilo there was no sign.

They stood well out to sea and sailed south, away from horror, to the ice-cold seas and known dangers of the Horn.

Once again Baines's luck had held. And continued to hold. At 80° 30′ west, 56° 20′ south they made their easting beneath clear blue skies and a fresh south-westerly coming over the quarter. Five days later they doubled the Horn and entered the slate-grey waters of the Atlantic.

The ice had moved far north this year. By night they could see the loom of its reflected light blinking beyond the horizon. By day it was a soft milky glare. For these were not the pygmy bergs of the northern hemi-sphere, but the true giants of the south. Great slabs of ice, ten miles long and a thousand feet high, peeled off from the Antarctic shelf.

Field ice lay flat on the sea, bobbing about the ship, occasionally grinding against the side while the hands tried to fend it off with poles and boat hooks.

Baines, hands clasped behind his back, slowly paced the poop, brows furrowed in thought as he wrestled with the problem. To the east the ice seemed to be thickening and he had no wish to be trapped, and possibly crushed, in an ice field. Ahead was the low rocky outline of Staten Island. Bare and uninhabited, blasted by wind, it guarded the entrance to the Strait of Le Maire, a short but turbulent stretch of water between the island and Tierra del Fuego. The Admiralty Sailing Directions gave the northerly tidal current as nine knots and warned against its passage. But it saved a sweep out into the Atlantic and many Cape Horners had chanced their arm and lived to tell the tale. With a fresh south-wester plus the nine-knot current, Baines calculated that he could be through in a couple of hours providing the Strait was clear of ice.

They approached the southern tip of Staten Island under lower topsails, ready to come about. Baines, peering intently ahead, caught a glimpse of a welter of white water funnelling itself through the passage. It shouldn't be too risky, sailing through a strait thirty miles long and twelve miles wide. He concentrated his gaze: there was not a sign of ice.

He made his decision. 'Very well, Mr Tranter, we'll take her through.'

Under topsails and royals, outer and flying jibs, the *Pampero* spread her wings and entered the Strait.

To port, blue-black mountains riven with ice gullies, capped with clouds, rose in ridges and bastions of iron-hard rock. To starboard lay the unimaginable desolation of Staten Island. It looked as though a giant hand had spilled a box of child's building blocks into the sea. The pressure of water forcing itself through the gate created a maelstrom of eddies and cross currents, snarling around the rocks, bursting in towers of spray. Current fought swell, throwing up vast perpendicular waves, to fall and leap again on the same spot. The accustomed rolling and pitching gave way to a series of short staggering lurches as the *Pampero* again and again smashed into the mad seas. The ocean poured through like a mill-race carrying all before it. Three men clung to the kicking wheel, striving to keep her on course as the stern yawed from side to side pushed by monstrous forces.

She was plunging along at sixteen knots and was more than half-way through when suddenly the wind dropped.

Baines paled and his mouth dried; his big hands gripped the rail until the knuckles threatened to burst through the skin.

The helmsmen spun the wheel. 'She's not answering, sir.' They looked to 'Lucky' Baines, every bit as frightened as he.

Baines stood, bereft of speech, frozen of action. There was nothing, literally nothing, he could do. The *Pampero* was already turning broadside on, as helpless as a piece of driftwood.

She careered on for a while with the sea clawing at her sides, while the sails drooped and flapped idly. Again and again she struggled like a thing alive to bring her head around; but the forces in play were too strong. She fought yard by yard, heaving and tossing, struggling to reach the gateway to the open sea a few short miles ahead.

She almost made it; then a narrow shelf of foam-flecked rock touched her stern. For a moment the ship shuddered then, pulling herself free, pointed her prow to the north and home. It seemed to be no more than a graze, and Baines expelled a breath he had been holding for an age. Then the *Pampero* sighed and began to settle slowly by the stern as the sea gurgled in. Still the ship would not give in. Labouring heavily she turned her head toward a tiny sheltered cove. Then the sea picked her up and wedged her bows between two pinnacles of rock.

They could hear the rend and wrench of timbers and feel the water pouring in.

Then the *Pampero* died.

Incongruously Baines had a vision of a mule collapsing and dying, neck out-stretched, tongue lolling in the dust of a sun-baked plaza. He tried to pull himself together. There was only one order left to give.

'Abandon ship, Mr Tranter.' His voice

was barely a whisper. Tears began to trickle down his face.

They took what stores they could and rowed away to the north, to Cape San Diego. There they would light distress fires, and sooner or later a passing vessel would pick up those who survived.

Baines looked back. The *Pampero*, wedged in her grave of rock, waited for the sea to pick her clean. He watched until the blue mountains shrouded her in shadow. Then she was gone.

Baines's luck had run out.

CHAPTER 14

ROBERT surveyed his new domain with a proprietorial air. There was no gainsaying it, the extended premises were a marked advance upon the old shop.

'A step into the future,' he told Sarah, portentously. 'A step into the future.'

Together they stood watching the signpainter completing his handiwork:

'ROBERT ONEDIN
High Class Grocer & Provision Merchant'

in gold-leaf lettering above the Cotton Hey window. Around the corner similar curlicues of gold announced:

'ROBERT ONEDIN
Ship Chandler & Wholesale Merchant'

to the dock road traffic.

The alterations had, indeed, been quite extensive and the new shop, its doors now opening upon the corner, seemed to suffer from a split personality as though not entirely sure of its station in life. Sides of bacon, dusted with rice flour and shrouded in butter-muslin as protection against the ever-present flies, hung outside the grocery window, while round the corner the chandlery window peeped uneasily through festoons of seaboots, oilskins, hanks of rope, lobster pots and oil lamps.

Inside, the grocery department, presided over by two assistants in white-bibbed aprons, claimed the space to the right; the bacon counter with its cool marble slab stacked with butter and cheeses ran the breadth of the shop to meet the provisions counter at right angles. Here were displayed shallow trays of coffee beans and tins of cocoa and lead-lined samples of tea, flanked by boxes of dried apricots, sultanas and raisins. And over all the mingled aromas of nutmeg, cinnamon, turmeric and senna tantalised the nostrils and tempted the appetites of indecisive customers.

Opposite, the chandlery department disappeared into a fog of paraffin, wax, colza oil and disinfectant. Regiments of boots and shoes stood to attention on racks behind mahogany counters. Barrels of flour and biscuit stood guard over bolts of canvas and coils of new manilla. A dozen brass chronometers ticked a dozen different times, and an equal number of compasses pointed to an equal diversity of north magnetic poles. This side of the business was officered by two grey-bearded assistants, as alike as twins, and wearing identical liveries of brass-buttoned waistcoats and green baize aprons. Thus the premises catered for two classes of customer, who met in a democratic swirl about the glass-fronted cash desk set in the geographic centre of the shop.

From the beginning it was obvious, to their delight and relief, that their new venture was proving a success; the two departments actually complementing rather than clashing with each other, as they had at first feared. Not infrequently a customer, arriving to purchase a pound of butter and a pint of peas, would wander across to the chandler's side and leave with the addition of a pair of shoes, or a box of handkerchiefs—for already haberdashery was proving a quite profitable sideline. Another, buying a pair of seaboots, would follow his nose to the grocery side and depart with a bag of coffee beans and a pound of bacon.

It was, Robert and Sarah agreed, clutching one another's hands for support once the initial shock of opening was over, a positively brilliant inspiration to put several departments under one roof. Why, there was no end to the possibilities!

'A millinery department!' breathed Sarah.

'Drapery!' pronounced Robert.

'Soft-furnishings! Fabrics! Curtain materials!'

'And wines and spirits! High class provisions and quality wines go together like—like biscuits and cheese!' Robert declaimed.

'Mm,' said Sarah non-committedly and counselling: 'But we must learn to walk before we run,' bringing their dreams down to earth with a bump.

'It's a step into the future,' he repeated, sententiously. 'A step into the future.' He snapped open his watch. 'Callon will be expecting me. I'd best be off.'

Sarah nodded. 'Very well, dear, if you must. But I am sure I don't know what you two find to talk about.'

'Business,' said Robert. 'Callon has a very shrewd head for business.'

He took his leave and set off in search of a hansom. Sarah could keep an eye on the shop; and with a cook and a parlourmaid and a nursemaid for little Samuel the house could practically run itself.

If only James would stay away for ever, he mused, as he strolled along, he would manage very well. He invariably progressed better when left to his own devices. There was nothing wrong with being a shopkeeper. He liked being a shopkeeper. He enjoyed nothing better than talking to people, selling them things, being of service. He was content with his station in life; and determined, then and there, never again to be drawn into James's pestiferous schemes. James wasn't the only man with ambitions. He had his own share: take this new venture; he visualised a shop taking up an entire block and housing dozens of different departments. A sort of bazaar, but on a larger scale than anything yet envisaged.

A hansom ambled past. Robert waved his stick, gave the cabby Callon's address and settled back to continue his ruminations.

It was odd the way the wheels of commerce ran quite smoothly when James was away. That pettifogging clerk Tupman seemed to have the business at his fingertips and rarely troubled Robert for his opinion. Work on the steamship was proceeding apace—although, he must admit, not without strong opposition from Albert who wished to revert to his original design of no masts and two engines, in spite of their agreement.

'You gave your word,' Robert had reminded him. 'It was a death-bed promise and, therefore, sacrosanct.'

'But dammit!' Albert had shouted. 'Callon isn't dead! Nor is he chairman—you are!'

But Robert had remained firm. 'A promise is a promise. Furthermore, Callon talks uncommon good sense.'

'Wait until James returns!' Albert had retorted darkly, and taken himself off to the draughtsmen's loft to brood over the ship plans.

Callon had mellowed considerably after his stroke, and he and Robert had struck up a pleasant friendship. They would meet twice a week, John the manservant pushing the bath-chair around to Callon's club, where they would take lunch and Callon would offer the benefit of his advice. He was but a shadow of his former self, a shrunken bag of skin and bones, completely paralysed down one side. But the old indomitable spirit still showed itself in occasional flares of anger, and he still had the ability to strike terror into the office staff by descending upon them unexpectedly, snarling from his bath-chair, his solitary eye revolving around the office like a lighthouse beam; and, like a lighthouse beam, missing nothing. Agnew's grip tightened and the unfortunate clerks lived in mortal dread of instant dismissal.

Naturally it was quite beyond Callon's powers to act as chairman, but Robert made an excellent mouthpiece and the ship progressed in accord with Callon's wishes rather than Albert's.

Yes, thought Robert, clasping his hands behind his head, he had every reason to be satisfied. Recently Callon had proposed him for membership of the Chamber of Commerce, and his first after-dinner speech had been received favourably; very favourably indeed, in his own honest opinion. He discovered that he rather liked public speaking. He had, he would be the first to admit, quite a talent for it. He had worked in his phrase about applying the brake of commonsense to the juggernaut of ambition and thrown in one or two others for good measure. 'The grasping hand of avarice plundering the pockets of the business community in order to support an army of mendicants and ne'er-do-wells' was one which had drawn a particular round of applause.

The hansom crunched along the gravelled driveway of Callon's residence, and as the cabby opened the little trap above Robert's head and extended a grubby hand for the fare, the front door opened and a coupled of footmen carried the bath-chair down the steps.

Callon twisted his features into a lopsided grin and took Robert's hand. 'Good to see you, my boy. Good to see you.'

He wore a cape and plaid rug about his knees. A floppy black hat and a patch over one eye gave him a sinister piratical air. Often, on one of their little outings, he would frighten little children by suddenly raising the eye-shield and revealing his stare-eye. In truth, he frightened the nursemaids more than the children, who would crowd around him, shrieking: 'Uncle Callon! Do it again, do it again! Show us your eye!'

They were making their way down to Bold Street packed with fashionable shoppers and choked with traffic, when the door to Mme Fauvière's millinery shop opened and Elizabeth stepped almost directly into their path.

New bonnets, again! thought Robert, and doffed his hat politely.

'Why, Robert! And dear Mr Callon!' Elizabeth exclaimed, clutching her parcels. 'I trust you are well, sir?' she inquired of Callon.

'As well as might be expected, and the brighter for seeing a pretty face,' replied Callon, gallantly.

They remained engaged in inconsequential conversation for a minute or two, damming the pavement while a river of passers-by flowed around them.

Elizabeth was about to take her leave when a cab, threading its way through a maze of carts and horses and carriages and broughams, caught the hub of its axle in the spokes of the off-side wheel of a brewer's dray. The cab slewed, one of the thin shafts broke, the horse squealed and reared, lost its footing and tumbled to the road, pitching the cab on its side.

A passing constable immediately ran to the horse, calming the beast's threshings by sitting on its head while the cabby picked himself up from the pavement and hurried to release his passengers trapped inside.

They stood watching as interested bystanders, while other onlookers called out a medley of advice.

To their astonishment the first figure to emerge was unmistakably that of Albert, to be followed by a series of hat boxes and parcels, some of which had burst open to reveal, in a froth of frills and laces, an assortment of garments instantly recognisable as a lady's nether habiliments.

Elizabeth had opened her mouth to speak, but it remained gaping wide as a voice called out from the depths of the interior: 'All right, Albert, me love. Give us a hand up, me darling. Careful where you put yer 'ands now! I'm only a working girl!'

Albert still had his back to them as he leaned over and dipped his arms into the cab. 'Ups-a-daisy!' he said, and, like a conjuror pulling a gigantic rabbit from a hat, rose with his hands at the waist of a laughing, delectable creature of raven-black hair and carmined lips.

Robert's tongue clove to the roof of his mouth and he prayed that Albert would not turn round or, if turning, would prove not to be Albert but a remarkable likeness. He knew exactly where he had seen the baggage before—accompanying Albert in that confounded restaurant. And now their sins had come home to roost with a vengeance!

Somewhat dishevelled, with a saucy bonnet hanging over one eye and squealing with laughter, she allowed herself to be swung to the pavement, displaying to the gaze of the vulgar a pair of red and white hooped stockings.

'Are you all right, my dear?' asked Albert considerately.

'No 'arm done, dear,' she said, straightening her bonnet and primping her hair. 'But it's give me a thirst like a bargee.' And burst into shrieks of laughter again.

Albert brushed down his clothes and then, with slow inevitability, turned his head. His gaze fell first upon Robert. He paused, ventured a half-smile, and then looked full at Elizabeth.

Robert, knowing his sister, waited for the explosion.

It never came. Pale with anger, she marched straight past Albert as though he didn't exist.

Callon's single eye roved from one to the other. 'Well,' he said, at last. 'There's no accounting for taste.'

Albert let himself in quietly, to find the servants scurrying about like frightened mice. He made his way upstairs, took a deep breath and squared his shoulders. Pushing open the bedroom door, he stepped inside to be met with a volley of Parian marble, Coalport vases and a selection of artificial fruit.

'Get out!' Elizabeth screamed. 'Get out! Get back to your damned doxy!'

'It is finished,' said Albert, protecting his head with extended arms.

'Finished!' she screeched. 'Finished! It should never have damned well started!'

'Be reasonable,' he pleaded.'

She brandished a brass poker. 'Keep

away from me. Keep your damned whore's tricks for others!'

'She meant nothing to me. She was nothing but a music-hall actress. We had a little fun, that's all, I swear.'

'You would swear your soul away, if it suited your purpose, Albert Frazer!'

'And you?' he demanded, coldly. 'What did you swear? Or have your forgotten Daniel Fogarty?'

'That was before we were married!'

'Really? You mean it doesn't count? At least, Claire won't be having my child,' he added, cruelly.

She spat at him. 'Get out! Get out, you damned libertine! Get out of my house!'

He opened the door, his own temper rising like bile. 'My house, madam. And you would do well to remember it!' The door slammed behind him.

She lay down across the bed, eyes scalded with tears and a black rage in her heart.

In the morning she rose after a sleepless night, called for the carriage and had herself driven to the shipyard and Albert's father.

He listened gravely, nodding his head from time to time.

'I understand your distress, my dear. But now you must put it behind you.'

'Never!' she said.

'You must, because there is no other way.'

'I must go back, and forgive him?'

'Not too readily, I imagine. But remember it is always easier to forgive than to be forgiven.'

She shook her head. 'I can't! I can't!'

'You came to me for advice. I am afraid this is the best I can offer. You deserve better than him, but neither of you can so easily escape your obligations. The young fool has made a public spectacle of himself and is no doubt smarting under the knowledge. It'll not happen again. Take my word for it.'

'What am I to do?' she wailed.

'New wounds become old wounds, given time to heal. I suggest you return home. Don't think of leaving him, not for one minute. For the world is a cruel place for a woman alone. Then there is the child to be considered. He needs a mother's love.'

'Yes,' she said, thoughtfully. 'There is always the child.' She came to her feet, jutting her jaw determinedly. 'Very well. I shall take your advice. But should there be any repetition . . .'

'There won't be,' said the old man, grimly. 'Not after I've finished with him.'

When Albert returned that evening she was waiting in the drawing room. There were dark circles beneath her eyes, but she had dressed with care in a becoming costume of dove grey, cut low to display her shoulders.

'I have decided to forget it,' she told him.

He put his arms about her. 'Thank you, my dear. Thank you. I don't deserve you. I don't really.'

She forced a smile and allowed him to kiss her. 'It's all over now,' she said. 'All over.'

But I'll make you pay, she swore silently to herself. By heaven, I'll make you pay!

CHAPTER 15

WITH Anjer dropping astern, the *Medusa* and *Pandora* headed north-north-east to round Billiter Island and beat through the passage between Vansittart Shoal with its foam of breakers surrounding sharp black teeth, and the low-lying, palm-covered banks of Emberton Island. They then set course for the Datu Islands at the north-west tip of Borneo.

'And with luck,' James told Anne cheerfully, 'you should catch your first glimpse of pirates.'

'Are they dangerous?' she asked, thinking of the unborn child.

'Dyaks,' he grinned. 'They collect heads. Don't be alarmed, we are too strong a force for them. They like easier pickings.'

She summoned up a smile. 'Poor Emma. She will be terrified.'

'If Daniel has any sense, he'll not enlighten her,' said James, watching the carpenter making a grating for the galley door, and the job watch engaged in greasing the masts and oiling the yard trusses.

She lingered on deck for a few minutes longer, enjoying the warm gentle breeze and the peace and solitude of shipboard life. Then she went below, picked up her sewing and settled herself comfortably on the settee to enjoy her favourite panoramic view through the great curve of the open stern windows. Away to the west lightning flickered and flared beyond the horizon. A small island of waving palms slid past on the port side. Half a dozen proas nosed out like a small shoal of inquisitive fish, then returned, bucking slightly in the ship's wash.

She had always imagined the China Sea to be a vast empty ocean rimmed by the mysterious mainland of the Far East. Instead it was a sea peppered with islands and atolls, shoals and reefs, and alive with craft of all shapes and sizes: dhows with high sterns and enormous lateen sails, lumbering junks with square sails of slatted bamboo; there were graceful Greek polaccas with light gaily-painted hulls and tall slender masts, sturdy Portuguese barcos and Javanese prau mayangs with rounded hulls and huge lug-lateen sails, British and

Yankee clippers beating south, and colourful Thai twakos with battened lugsails, sharply raked foremasts, and all-seeing eyes painted on the bows.

It seemed as though the ships of every nation in the world had met in this one stretch of water, all bound for the fabled riches of the East.

She was dozing pleasantly when there came a polite tap on the door. In answer to her reply Mr Armstrong stood on the threshold, grinning hugely and rubbing his hands together in barely-contained excitement.

'Cap'n's compliments, ma'am; and would you be pleased to come on deck.'

Wonderingly, she followed Armstrong out into the oven-heat and glare of sunlight on the deck above. Once her eyes had adjusted to the blaze of day, she became aware of an unusual stir of activity. The watch below had tumbled out and were being armed with cutlasses and muskets while the watch on deck were busily loading and running out the two brass cannons.

'What is it?' she asked.

'Look,' he said, pointing.

She screwed her eyes and saw that the smaller craft, junks and praus were scattering like a flock of sheep before a pack of wolves.

'There are your pirates,' he said casually. She looked again. They were quite unlike any pirate vessel she had ever imagined. Each was about fifty feet long with a tripod mast forward, a high thatch-covered poop and a long bowsprit with a triangular jib. The head of the single mainsail was laced to an extremely long yard and the foot laced to a boom. Attached to the yards were long black tufts streaming out like horse's manes. Suddenly she realised they were hanks of human hair.

'Malays,' James was saying. 'Flying-praus. Keep your head down,' he warned. 'I fancy one of 'em carries a swivel gun.'

There were three of them. Rakish-looking craft, skimming over the water at deceptive speed. Even as James spoke there came a sharp bang and the foremast prau emitted a puff of smoke. The sea between suddenly kicked up in a flurry of tiny spouts.

'Out of range,' said James placidly. 'Fire

when you are ready, Mr Llewellyn,' he called to the second mate.

Llewellyn was standing in the waist, blowing upon a smouldering length of tarred hemp. He raised a hand in salute, squinted along the gun, then brought the glowing end to the touch-hole. The boom of the cannon almost deafened her as it erupted in a spurt of flame and a cloud of black smoke. Then she became aware of a thin whistling through the air. Seconds later the leading prau's mainsail disappeared into a thing of shreds and tatters. The vessel yawed and flew up into the wind as the second cannon roared. Again the air was filled with that strange, ominous whistling, then the prau's mast sheered off and fell over the side. A number of brown bodies, dancing and capering on deck, suddenly turned crimson and hurtled backwards among their companions.

'By God,' said James, jubilantly. 'Your father should be here now. He'd enjoy every minute of this.'

The other two praus had altered course, slipped out of range, but were now converging upon their disabled companion.

'Reload,' James commanded. 'Fire when you are ready.'

She clutched his arm. 'No, James, no! They are giving succour! You must not!'

'Fire!' called James. 'Fire and reload. Mr Armstrong, stand by to come about. We shall close the range, if you please.'

The two brass cannons belched and leaped back on their trunnions. The air filled again with the scream of shot. The deck of one of the relieving praus turned into a shambles of threshing limbs, blood and sinews, splinters flew high in the air, mast and sails crumpled to drape the vessel like a shroud.

She turned her head away and saw the gun crews, smoke-blackened and grinning, swabbing out the muzzles, ramming home the cartridges, then stuffing canvas bags of—something? She frowned in perplexity.

'Chain shot,' James told her, following the direction of her gaze. 'Mixed with a few bolts, shackle pins and a handful of nails.'

'Cuts 'em up a treat, ma'am,' said Armstrong, shark-mouth wide in a grin of approval.

The *Medusa* was already coming round

smartly and rapidly closing the distance. A shadow moved between them and the sun as the *Pandora* glided swiftly to take up station to windward of the remaining prau. Bright flashes followed by a ragged volley of musket fire rippled from its decks. Then the *Medusa*'s guns roared once more. She put her hands over her eyes.

'Cease firing,' said James. He put an arm about her shoulders. 'It's all over.'

She forced herself to open her eyes again. The three praus were now nothing but a tangle of shattered, water-logged hulks, slowly rising and falling in an ever-widening red lake. A few survivors clung to the wreckage. The surrounding sea was littered with debris and brown bodies turning and swaying in the swell.

'Bring her back to course, if you please, Mr Armstrong,' he commanded.

'Aren't we going to pick them up?' she asked.

He clasped his hands behind his back. 'No. If we do, they will either be hung by the British, or beheaded by the Chinese. If we leave them . . .' He shrugged. 'They have a chance.'

She hated to question his judgement, but

300

she knew she would worry away at the problem unless she received an answer.

'James. Was it necessary to fire upon those remaining vessels? Pirates they may have been, but they were only trying to render aid to their companions.'

'Do you see that junk?'

She followed his pointing arm to a vermilion and gold hull wallowing sluggishly, ungainly sails flapping in the light airs, long sweeps flailing the water as it struggled, like some strange overburdened insect, to escape from the scene.

'Yes.'

'Thirty or forty people live on board. Men, wives and children. Had we allowed just one of those praus to escape, that junk would have been taken and every soul aboard slaughtered. What would be your choice? To save the innocent, or the guilty?'

She nodded. He was right, of course. He was always right.

'I'm only sorry,' he said, 'that you were exposed to the spectacle. But I never expected their chief to be so reckless and foolhardy as to come within range of a British ship.'

She looked from the junk to their own

ship. Her heart suddenly beat painfully. 'They were attacking us?'

'It's very rare,' he assured her. 'Their chief was a fool. Probably wanted to gain a reputation for daring among his people.' He smiled grimly. 'He'll not try again.'

They sailed on but both ships took the precaution of rigging boarding nets and doubling the look-outs, and twenty-four hours later with the wind freeing and the yards sharp up they cruised through a scattered group of islands and put in at Datu.

The ships lay motionless in the grip of light and heat while they took on fresh water, fruit, a couple of dozen live fowls and a cask of pickled eggs.

Emma, far from being distressed by their recent encounter, seemed to look upon the whole affair as a spectacle arranged for her especial benefit and had clapped and cheered as loudly as any seaman at the bloody destruction. Her only regret was that Daniel had not had the forethought to arm themselves also with a cannon and she demanded that he rectify the omission at the earliest opportunity.

She displayed not the slightest interest in

her surroundings, but sat admiring Anne's spacious cabin and complaining of the heat which she found particularly enervating. In fact, the term 'enervating' had become the keystone of her vocabulary and was applied indiscriminately to everything which offended her comfort. The food was enervating, the sea was enervating, the climate—above all—was enervating. Even dear Daniel was enervating. The natives she lumped together as untutored savages not worthy of recognition as members of the human race, and simply sniffed disparagingly and changed the subject when Anne gently pointed out that although it was true that they lived in a state of nature, they were quite obviously contented with their lot and evinced nothing but goodwill toward the intruders.

'Intruders? Us?' Emma seemed exasperated at the notion. 'They are heathens and cannibals,' she pronounced dismissively and launched into her favourite topic: What were they doing at home? At this very minute? What would the ladies be wearing? The shops displaying? She prattled on, boring Anne to distraction until, by way of stopping a flow of reminiscences about long-past parties and balls, she interrupted to announce: 'I believe I am with child.' Immediately she could have bitten off her tongue, for certainly such a chatterbox as Emma would lose no time in spreading the gossip about both ships. Now she must tell James immediately.

Emma stopped in mid-flow. Her eyes widened and her hand went to her mouth. 'Oh, how dreadful for you!' she exclaimed. 'Really, men are wicked, wicked brutes with no thought beyond the satisfaction of their own pleasures!'

Anne was startled at Emma's outburst. It had never occurred to herself or James that pleasure played its part in the necessary business of producing children. It was ordained by Testament, and that was enough.

Emma was counting upon her fingertips; she stared in dismay at the result. 'You must persuade James to turn about immediately, otherwise it might very well be born aboard ship. How awful!'

'The child will be born in Liverpool,' said Anne confidently. 'I have calculated most carefully.'

'Daniel can bully as much as he likes. But

I shan't take the risk,' said Emma. 'It is too dreadful to contemplate. Oh, you poor, poor creature,' she sympathised.

Anne felt anger rising. She was sure that she would strike the vapid little ninny if she was forced to share her company much longer. She managed a false smile and came to her feet.

'I think we are about to get under way,' she announced, and escorted Emma on to deck.

James, busy overseeing the stowage of a couple of squealing porkers, raised a hand in farewell. Emma turned a haughty nose in the air and stepped delicately down the companion ladder to the waiting boat.

'What's the matter with Emma?' he asked Anne as she stood by his side watching the bustle of activity as baskets of paw-paws, yams and coconuts were hoisted aboard from the waiting bumboats.

Anne shrugged. 'The poor child is unhappy.'

'She's a spoiled brat,' said James unfeelingly, and pointed to a raucous cockerel, its head raised above the wicker frame of its pen as it gave voice to its feelings. 'We'll have him for supper.'

She bit her lip. 'James—?'

'Mm?' He suddenly jumped into activity to leap across the deck and pounce upon a native about to slice off a few fathoms of line from one of the *Medusa*'s downhauls. The man wriggled like an eel from James's grasp and went over the side in an arc-ing dive.

James returned, scratching his head ruefully. 'You need eyes like a hawk. They are a parcel of thieves, every man-jack of 'em. What were you saying?'

'I was about to remark that I believe your son should be born in Liverpool.'

'Good, good,' he replied absently, his attention elsewhere. Then he blinked. 'What—what did you say?'

Smilingly she repeated her information.

'Good grief! You mustn't—you shouldn't—you can't! I mean—'

Her smile broadened at his consternation. 'You must not concern yourself so, James.'

'Concern? Of course I'm concerned! Good God, woman, do you know what you are saying?'

She nodded complacently. 'There is no doubt.'

'You must remain calm,' he said, shaking

306

from head to foot. 'Calm. That's the ticket! Remain calm. You must not exert yourself,' he told her, calmly banging his hands together and hopping from one foot to another. 'You must go below and lie down.'

'Not immediately, James. Perhaps in another six or seven months I might take your advice, but for the moment I think I will stay on deck.'

'Six or seven months?' He screwed his features into a frown of concentration. 'A hundred-day passage home—can't count on less—trade around the coast—wait for the tea harvest—loading time. By God, Anne, but you are cutting it fine!'

'It will be all right, James,' she promised gravely. 'Do not distress yourself.'

He gulped, looked around for inspiration, then nervously touched her arm as though she might fall to pieces at any moment. 'You must really get out of this heat, my dear. It is . . .'

'Enervating?' she suggested.

'That is exactly the word. Enervating. You must on no account permit yourself to be enervated,' he instructed, and stared in surprise at her sudden peal of laughter.

They sailed an hour before sunset and at noon the following day tacked to the east to clear the lonely bulk of Bunguran Island. Then they headed north across a sea which by day sparkled beneath an oriental sun, and by night glowed with phosphorescence, their wakes leaving comet-trails of golden fire, while the moon hung like a yellow lantern in a velvet sky pricked with stars.

The airs were light, and boxed around the compass. Sudden squalls, dead calms, and baffling winds kept the watch busy trimming yards, setting and taking in sails.

At the end of three exasperating days they had covered a bare two hundred miles; then the wind suddenly strengthened, hauled to east-south-east, and a scarlet and green macaw fell out of the sky to collide with the mizzen rigging and tumble on to deck, from which position it snapped its nutcracker beak viciously at all and sundry. After a while it took to strutting about, uttering harsh plaintive cries and cocking a puzzled eye at this strange floating island with trees bare of foliage. Eventually it flew off with rapid beats of its wings; a flash of colour that disappeared into the glare of the sun. A couple of hours later they passed it again, bobbing in the water, wings outspread, sightless eyes glazed in reproach.

The ship picked up speed under royals and stunsails, and James set the watch to lacing the foot of the upper topsails to the jackstays of the lower topsail yards. The *Medusa* began to creep away from the *Pandora*; then Fogarty rigged two long topmast studdingsail booms and the *Pandora* once again closed the distance.

James grinned. They were like two fencers, probing each other's style before the cut and thrust of the duel.

At 8 a.m. the following morning they sighted the southernmost shoal of the dangerous Paracels, a hundred square miles of hidden reefs, half-submerged atolls and sandbanks straggling across the main sea route to Hong Kong and the Treaty ports of China.

The two ships altered course as one and cleared the Paracels to the west. Four days later they dropped anchor in Hong Kong roads, and while the ships again replenished their stores, James and Daniel had themselves rowed ashore to arrange for their clearance papers and obtain the ships' Chop, or official seal, permitting them to trade from certain specified ports. In effect it was little more than a face-saving device, for following the defeat of the Dragon Army at the gates of Tien-Tsin two years ago, effective resistance had ceased, and today the ships of the barbarians swarmed about the coast like locusts.

The island of Hong Kong at the mouth of the Pearl River towered in green folds from an iridescent sea. White bungalows with long cool verandahs were sprinkled across the heights, while down at the shoreline banking houses and warehouses rubbed shoulders with pagoda-roofed tea houses and sing-song houses. And lapping the wharves was a floating city of sampans, lighters and junks, teeming with life, voices a low humming as though from a multitude of beehives. Smoke from cooking pots curled lazily to a lapis-lazuli sky and rich, unfamiliar odours drifted across a harbour packed with shipping—tea clippers, island schooners, opium traders from India, troopships and shallow-draught gunboats, fishing boats, junks and a wood-fired ferry boat chugging its way across to Macao at the tip of the mainland opposite.

Sampans with roofs of woven matting surrounded the *Medusa* like a village market, with the shopkeepers shouting their wares in shrill high-pitched voices. Anne and Emma, peering over the side, were simultaneously gripped with a fever of bargaining. Possessed by the madness of acquisition they showered silver and gold upon the fortunate merchants in return for pots of preserved ginger, heathen idols carved in jade, pictures created of peacock feathers and butterfly wings, porcelain jars, intricately carved ivory fans, tortoiseshell combs, parasols of oiled silk, tiny, fragile tea sets of egg-shell china, yards of embroidered silks, bolts of shantung, nests of lacquered boxes, delicate water-colours of dreamlike landscapes, tea-gowns, carpets, silver bracelets, paper flowers and finally, when their money had run out, voices hoarse with bargaining, they invested their last few farthings in a couple of coolie hats.

When James and Daniel returned, hot and dusty from their journey to the residency at the top of the mist-shrouded

Peak, they found Anne and Emma gazing enrapt at a treasure house of possessions strewn across the cabin floor. Each wore a large straw hat, was swathed in silk and swayed from side to side emitting sudden giggles and unladylike belches as they sipped from tiny teacups.

Daniel picked up a bottle of rice wine and turned it upside down. He stared at James. 'Good grief! They are as drunk as fishes!'

Emma weaved unsteadily to her feet, focused upon Daniel with difficulty and enunciated clearly: 'That is a wicked, cruel aspersion, Daniel Fogarty, when it is plain for all to see that we are quite simply dreadfully enervated by the weather. If I were a gentleman I would call you out for that, sir.'

Daniel grinned. 'If you were a gentleman, my dear, I doubt we should be married.'

She waved an accusing finger and lurched toward him. 'Marriage, and the marriage bed! The one thought in your mind! And yet, did you, or did you not promise that we would wed of convenience?' He speech thickened and she waved an arm as though brushing cobwebs from her eyes. 'Deny it, if you dare!'

'That is enough, Emma,' said Daniel, sharply. 'Come, I shall escort you back to the ship.' He held out an arm, but she pushed him aside.

'I find your very touch repugnant.'

Daniel's temper flared. 'Come along, little Miss Precious,' he snapped, and pushed her roughly toward the door.

She fell to her knees. 'I want to go home,' she wailed. 'I want to go home.'

Daniel looked helplessly toward Anne and James. 'I'm sorry. I am afraid my wife is not quite herself.'

Emma clasped her arms about her shoulders and rocked forwards and backwards. 'Poor Daniel,' she wept. 'Poor Daniel. My fault. I'm no wife. No wife at all. I treat him dreadful cruel, and he forgives me; always forgives me. Poor Daniel.'

Daniel hefted her to her feet. 'It's all right, Emma,' he said gently. 'I understand. Come along, my dear. Let me take you back to the ship.'

She nodded contritely, reached out a

hand and stroked his face. 'Dear Daniel,' she murmured. 'Dear Daniel.'

Daniel, awkward with embarrassment, bade a brusque good night and, shepherding a stumbling Emma before him, left them alone.

James scratched his head and looked down at Anne. 'Well, well,' he commented. 'It seems young Daniel's picked a Tartar for himself.'

Anne was concentrating on tracing the pattern of a Chinese rug. She hiccuped. 'I think I want to lie down,' she pronounced slowly.

James grinned. 'You are lying down,' he said.

Once aboard the *Pandora* Daniel saw Emma safely to their room, dumped her unceremoniously on the bed, then, speechless with rage, took himself off for a turn on deck and a final cigar.

Pacing slowly up and down, face clenched in thought, he brooded over the circumstances that had brought him to this pass—married to a wife as cold as ice and temperamental as a child, and engaged in a race for the outcome of which he cared little. Callon, he realised belatedly, had been responsible for the one, and James for the other. He had a sense of being manipulated by others; of being carried along on the tide of other people's ambitions. For his own part, he acknowledged, he was a man of small ambitions; he would have been more than content to remain master of the *Barracuda*. The *Barracuda* and Elizabeth to wife—her image suddenly burst into his mind like a flame, and memories tumbled like meteors—her arms reaching out from the near-darkness, her voice crooning with desire, her body leaping, leaping beneath his . . . He crushed the cigar and threw it into the sea. She had promised her undying love, then married that popinjay Albert. While he—well, he had married an heiress, and for the life of him he couldn't understand why.

He returned below, and in the privacy of their private bathroom stripped, washed himself down and put on a clean nightshirt.

He thought Emma to be asleep when he tiptoed into their sleeping quarters, but although she was lying still and quiet beneath the covers, her open eyes glinted in the pale silver of moonlight. She stirred as he moved back the covers, then surprisingly raised her arms. 'Dear Daniel,' she murmured. 'It will be all right. I promise.'

For a moment he did not understand. Then her hands reached to his head and drew him down.

'I've been a fool, Daniel,' she whispered. 'Wife me. Please, Daniel. Please wife me.'

CHAPTER 16

FROM Hong Kong they sailed north to
Shanghai where they took on a cargo
of rice for Swatow. Rice was fetching
80 cents a pical, or sixty shillings a ton and
James rubbed his hands as the last bag was
slung aboard. 'This is where we cover our
expenses,' he told Anne. 'A few more loads
like this and we'll show a profit.'

Anne was puzzled. 'I thought the race
was to Foochow?'

'Who cares about a beaver hat?' he
exclaimed. 'I've no doubt but that Keay's
engaged in the same trade.'

'I mean, tea,' she said. 'I thought we
should be loading tea for home.'

'The moment the crop is ready, we shall
be there. But in the meantime, there are
profits to be earned.'

The *Pandora*'s cargo was for Wenchow,
and a few miles off-shore the ships parted
company.

'Never fear,' said James. 'We shall meet
again at Foochow.'

From Swatow they sailed in ballast to

Yokohama in the newly opened country of Japan, to load once again with rice, this time for Whampoa.

The Japanese were a fierce warlike race, not in the least overawed by the might of the West. Even the coolies toiling in the depths of the hold refused to be brow-beaten, and when one of the *Medusa*'s seamen playfully kicked one of the loading gang, staggering beneath the burden of a hundredweight sack of rice, the man turned upon his tormentor and sliced open his ribs from armpit to waist with a long double-edged knife carried in the waistband of his trousers.

Twenty-five days later they were back at Hong Kong where they discharged their rice, loaded with shingle ballast and, at last, sailed for Foochow.

Dawn was peeling open the sky as they rounded Turnabout Island and entered the Min River where they took on the Chinese pilot, a Mr Liu Hing, an affable smiling man in a suit of poojong and of a limited command of English.

'Savvy plenty water. Can go,' he announced cheerfully as he clambered over the side. But he seemed to know his business, for they proceeded upriver without mishap, skirting rocks and shoals, and taking every advantage of a tide that ran like a sluice.

Anne, seated on her deck chair, thought the scenery magnificent. On either side hill rose above hill, each one terraced and cultivated to the summit. Along the banks were scattered small fishing villages, mud forts and josshouses. Women and children washed and bathed and waved at the flying-dragon ship. Timber-laden polejunks, moored at piles, waited for the tide to turn. Rice boats and cooking boats plied from village to village, while sampans turned sluggishly in the backwaters.

Liu Hing pointed ahead to water bubbling and foaming over a sandbar. 'Chow-chow water,' he told them, still smiling, and making chopping motions with his hands. 'Plenty chow-chow water. We go.'

They bumped over the sandbar, rounded a bend in the river, and there before them lay Foochow.

The foreign settlement had long been established on Nantai Island, a green-clad oasis separating the turbulent waters of the river and connected to the mainland by two delicately arched bamboo bridges. Foochow proper, the tea-port, sprawled along the cliffs of the northern bank, and half a dozen clippers were already waiting in the curve of the Pagoda Anchorage.

The *Pandora* had evidently arrived before them and lay below the rest of the fleet, close to the Pagoda Rock.

The pilot waved his hands. 'All go,' he said. 'Soon plenty tea come chop-chop.'

James raised and lowered his arm in a signal to Mr Armstrong on the fo'c's'le head. Armstrong waved acknowledgement and a moment later the port anchor leapt from the cat-head to plunge to the river bed and send up clouds of muddy water. With fore and main topsails clewed up, James ordered the helm down, hauled down the jib and flattened the spanker. The *Medusa* turned, met the tide, leaned back and took the strain on her cable. Then the starboard anchor fell with a splash, the hands paid out more cable and she settled comfortably, just bucking the tideway.

Leaving the rest of the business of mooring fore and aft in Armstrong's capable hands, James stepped across to

Anne and held out a hand to help her to her feet.

He really is the most considerate of men, she thought, as she took his grip and allowed him to pull her to her feet. Then suddenly, unexpectedly, a sudden wrench of pain brought a gasp to her lips.

He viewed her with anxiety. 'What is it?'

'Nothing,' she replied quickly. 'Just a stitch.'

She must have replied too quickly, for he showed even more concern. 'I shall send for the doctor. In the meantime you must go below and rest.'

Too alarmed to argue, she allowed herself to be conducted below where she undressed and changed into her nightshift. It was only at that point that she became obstinate, flatly refusing to go to bed until the doctor actually set foot aboard.

'It's so dismal lying abed when I could as easily rest here,' she told him, taking up her favourite position by the stern windows. 'I can occupy myself with a little sewing and at the same time keep a weather eye open for the arrival of the doctor's launch.'

'Mm,' said James, pulling thoughtfully

at his chin. 'He's more likely to arrive in a sampan and speak pidgin English.'

He was right on the first count, and almost on the second. Dr McKrae's sampan had an awning of red silk emblazoned with Chinese characters and was poled by two boatmen in blue cotton uniforms. The learned doctor wore a top hat of plaited straw and a loose-fitting, wide-sleeved green robe over an ill-fitting suit of shantung. He spoke quickly to his aides in cackling Chinese, apparently reserving his native tongue—strong enough to raise dust from a carpet—for his patients.

He was a red-haired, freckle-faced, middle-aged man with a fringe of ginger whiskers and a brandy breath, and certainly lacked the bedside manner of Dr Parslow; but his examination was swift and sure. He returned his ancient wooden stethoscope to a jumble of other museum-pieces in his medical bag, mumbled what appeared to be a series of incantations to himself, then perched beside Anne to listen attentively to the history of her complaint, interrupting only to put sharp-edged pertinent questions when she showed signs of evasion.

'Mmm,' he said, when she had finished. 'Mmm. Mmm. Mmm.' He sounded as though he were humming a little tune to himself. Then he sighed deeply. 'What can I possibly tell ye that yeer ain medical man back in Liverpool has not already tell't ye?' He sighed again. 'Yeer husband is a heartless fool; and I shall so inform him.'

'No,' said Anne quickly. 'You must not. He does not know.'

He stared at her in perplexity. 'Ye do understand the consequences?'

Anne bit her lip. 'He—he so longs for a son.'

He sighed once more and wagged his head at the folly and contrariness of human nature. 'It seems ye didna think of giving the poor man a choice.'

She considered for a moment. 'Is the risk, then, that grave?'

He faced her grimly. 'Ye have a tumour. I'll no hide it from ye—if the bairn is borned aboard ship I'll no' give a straw for your chances. If it's borned in Liverpool, and ye can obtain the best of medical attention, ye have a hope. Today they have chloroforms and antiseptics, and I hear they even boil their instruments.'

Her eyes searched his face. 'Will the child live?'

'That I canna answer. All I can tell ye is that there is nothing in your condition that precludes that possibeelity. But it is no' the health of the bairn that should be concerning us, Mistress Onedin.'

'It is my sole concern,' she stated flatly.

'Then it shouldna be. All life is precious. Including yeer ain,' he added drily.

Moving away from the bedside, he rummaged in his capacious bag. 'Out here on the Coast we have little in the way of modern medicines, but I have a Chinese concoction which I strongly recommend as a sovereign paregoric against the onset of pain which—I warn ye—will increase in frequency.'

'I understand,' she said calmly. 'It is an opiate.'

He fished out a couple of fluted bottles and stood them on the drop-leaf bedside table. 'Ye may call it that, if ye wish, but ye'll be grateful for its effect long before yeer time is come.'

'Will it—?'

'No, madam,' he said, anticipating her question. 'It will not have any deleterious consequences upon the health of the child. In the meantime ye'd do well to remember that it is your health that is of overriding importance. Your health,' he emphasised. 'Nothing else.' He picked up his bag. 'And now I shall have a wee word with yeer husband.'

'You won't tell him of—of my other condition?' she begged.

The doctor snorted and by way of answer yanked open the door. 'Ye may come in the noo, Captain Onedin.'

James stepped inside, cracking his knuckles in a fever of anxiety. 'How is she?' he demanded.

'As well as might be expected under the circumstances,' said McKrae, ambiguously. 'But I'd be happier in my mind if I could be assured that yeer wife would have her confinement in more civilised surroundings than those afforded by a ship.'

'How long do we have?'

'Young man, if ye canna answer that question yeersel' ye should never have embarked upon parenthood in the first place,' snapped McKrae, tartly. He nodded to Anne. 'I'll attend upon ye again before ye set sail, Mistress Onedin.'

James followed him out on to deck. 'Well?' he asked impatiently. 'What is your diagnosis?'

McKrae tugged at his chin whiskers. 'She has an ailment which will no doubt cause considerable discomfort during the course of time,' he conceded.

'Is it dangerous?'

'Childbirth is always dangerous,' McKrae replied obliquely, and clambered over the side to his waiting sampan. 'She needs rest and consideration,' he called as the boatmen poled away. 'Remember—rest and consideration.' His voice trailed away to be lost amid the distant echoing hills.

James returned below to find Anne in the act of dressing.

'The doctor said you must rest,' he told her.

'But he did not say that I must spend my days lying abed. That will no doubt come later. In the meantime I intend to avail myself of the opportunity of taking a short promenade ashore.'

He had not the heart to oppose her determination. 'Very well,' he told her. 'But you must not tire yourself. You shall travel by sampan and rickshaw. And I shall accompany you. I have business to conduct at our agents' hong. Later we can take tea together in the clubhouse.'

A sampan ferried them ashore where they transferred to a pair of sedan chairs carried on the shoulders of perspiring coolies who kept up a loping rhythmic pace to a panting chant of 'Whoo-ha—Whoo-ha—Whoo-ha!'

James had himself deposited at the doors of the business premises of Adamson and Bell & Co, who shared their hong with Jardine and Matheson.

At the top of the steps he met the jaunty figure of Captain Keay, who greeted him with a grin of welcome. 'Good afternoon, Onedin. I trust it has not escaped your recollection that you owe me a new beaver hat?'

'I have not forgotten,' replied James, grinning back. 'Double or quits for the return voyage?'

'Why not?' said Keay, as they shook hands. 'Two more to add to my collection.' He nodded affably and trotted away down the steps.

Inside the hong, the air was cool and fragrant with the scent of jasmine and sweet-smelling incense. Slatted bamboo blinds allowed a diffused golden light to penetrate the vastness of the office. Rows of Chinese clerks sat at long desks, drawing up manifests and bills of lading, rapidly inscribing strange mutilated characters with quick strokes of their camel-hair brushes.

He found Mr Peterson, the agent, seated at a lacquered desk at the far end of the building and engaged in conversation with Daniel Fogarty.

Peterson stood up and held out a hand as James approached.

'Ah—Captain Onedin. We have been discussing your problem. As you are no doubt aware every ship here is eager to be the first to load. However, I have just received a visit from Captain Keay who has put forward a proposition on behalf of the other masters. I will arrange that your two ships be loaded first and at one and the same time. There is but one condition: should either of you arrive home ahead of any of the other vessels you will agree to relinquish any bonus or prize money to the next ship to dock.'

'I have already agreed,' said Daniel.

'I agree,' said James.

'Very well, gentlemen,' said Peterson. 'Freight is quoted at seven pounds a ton.' He held out a hand. 'All that remains, gentlemen, is to wish you a fast passage and fair winds. I might add that already a great deal of money has been wagered on the outcome. I trust you will each give us a run for our money.'

'We shall do our best,' said Daniel.

'We'll do nothing until the tea arrives,' said the practical James, and turned to Fogarty. 'Shall we join the ladies?'

Anne and Emma were taking iced tea on the broad, cool verandah of the clubhouse when a perspiring Dr McKrae arrived and was making his way to an empty chair when he espied Anne. He changed direction, waited until Anne had presented Emma, then flopped into the basket chair opposite.

'I thought, young woman,' he pronounced, addressing himself to Anne, 'that I had advised complete rest.'

'I am resting,' she told him, smiling.

'Aye, I daresay ye'll find more comfort here than aboard ship.' He raised a hand and a Chinese waiter, pigtail bobbing, rope-soled slippers flap-flapping over the polished wood floor, appeared at his elbow.

'Gin sling,' he commanded, and opened his cigar case. 'Would you ladies permit an old man to indulge in his favourite vice?'

Anne laughed. 'Please do, Doctor. I can assure you that we are more than used to our respective husbands fumigating our quarters.'

'Thank ye kindly,' said McKrae, striking a match and contentedly puffing out clouds of blue smoke.

They chattered on inconsequentially until the waiter returned with a tall glass of effervescing liquid.

'What is it?' asked Emma.

'An alcoholic beverage, my dear. Bad for the kidneys, but good for the soul,' McKrae pronounced, drinking deeply.

'Could I try one, do you think?'

'As a medical practitioner, I recommend it,' said McKrae. He snapped his fingers for the departing waiter and turned to Anne.

'Mistress Onedin?'

'No, thank you,' said Anne, thinking of the baby.

McKrae burbled incomprehensibly at

the waiter and then resumed their conversation.

'Have you lived here long?' asked Emma, during a lull in his flow of reminiscences.

'Twenty-eight years,' he told them. 'And I intend to die here.'

'You have no wish to return to your place of birth?' queried Anne.

He shook his head. 'Never. This is my home.' He leaned forward and wagged his cigar accusingly. 'Ye come out in yeer fine ships, backed by the power of gunboats, demanding the freedom to trade. Trade is it!' He spat out a leaf of cigar. 'What d'ye have to offer that the Chinese do not already have? They grow all the food they need, clothe themselves better and more sensibly than any like family at home. Damnblast it, the country's self-supporting! Why the devil don't ye leave 'em alone!' He huffed and puffed and then apologised. 'I'm sorry, ladies, but it riles my spirit when I see uncouth barbarians contaminating a ceevilisation that was flourishing when they were running around in woad! We'll say no more, and change the subject.'

Emma cupped her chin on her hands.

She had, Anne thought, a sly look on her face.

'Is it true, Doctor, that the Chinese are adepts at making love potions?' She lowered her eyes and blushed.

'Aphrodisiacs, ye mean?' He drained his glass as the waiter returned with two more, placed one before Emma and handed the other to the doctor.

'Aye, my dear, they do have that reputation. If ye're wishful of exporting to 'em then I suggest ye load yeer ships wi' rhinoceros horn and the bones of the sea-unicorn.'

Emma looked disappointed. She sipped her drink. 'Is that all?'

'No,' he said. 'They are the most prized ingredients, but there are others which are claimed to be equally efficacious. I have no idea as to their ingredients, and not the slightest curiosity to find out.'

'Do they work?' asked Emma. She appeared to be inspecting the contents of her glass.

'They work if you believe they work,' said McKrae. He waved an expansive arm encompassing the hinterland. 'If ye require proof, it's oot there. There are more bairns borned in one day in China than the rest of the world put together.'

Emma considered for a moment. 'Do you drink it, or eat it, or what?'

McKrae shrugged. 'It doesna matter. It's the effect that counts. Why? Are ye thinking of slipping a wee potion to yer husband? The man's a dolt if he is in need of that kind of stimulation.'

'No, no,' said Emma, colouring furiously. 'No, quite the contrary. No, I didn't mean that—I mean . . .' She dipped her head and gulped down her drink. 'This is really quite delicious.' She raised her head and smiled. 'I hope this does not contain any of their wicked concoctions?'

He shook his head. 'That is plain Hollands and effervescent mineral water with the juice of a lemon. It's the home-produced stuff ye must beware of.'

'I shall take particular care,' said Emma, lightly.

At that moment a buzz of noise like the humming of a hive rose from the town opposite, ships' bells began to ring and the waiter scuttled across to gobble like a turkey in McKrae's ear.

McKrae beamed and came to his feet.

'The tea is coming! Permit me to escort you, ladies. It's a sight ye've never seen before, and may never see again, I'll be bound!'

They followed him to the high central arch of the bridge of Peaceful Fortune reaching to the northern bank.

Anne drew in a breath. To the sound of beating gongs a flotilla of heavily loaded sampans was heading downriver. But such a flotilla as she had never seen. The leading sampans were decorated with banners of crimson and gold, while paper dragons emitting clouds of smoke danced on their decks. Rockets seared into the sky, fire-crackers jumped and banged in startling arabesques, grotesquely masked dancers capered and whirled like dervishes. The rippling dragon tail twisted and turned to disappear around the far bend of the river and, as the head glided beneath the bridge, the ships' bells rose to a deafening clamour, while the setting sun, tipping the hills with orange light, brought sudden purple darkness punctuated by myriads of paper lanterns hanging out over the river at the ends of long poles.

Anne glanced up as James and Daniel

arrived, and together they stood watching spellbound as the cavalcade of boats fanned out across the anchorage to sweep down upon the waiting ships. Some peeled off to cluster in half-dozens about the *Falcon*, the *Min*, the *Flying Spur*, the *Robin Hood*, the *Fiery Cross* and the *Ellen Rodger* moored at the head of the harbour; the rest moved on to swarm about the *Medusa* and the *Pandora* until they resembled nothing other than a heaving platform of boats.

'I must return to the ship,' said James. 'There is work to be done, and no sleep until they have completed.'

They took their leave of Daniel and Emma and to the now familiar chant of the coolies, 'Whoo-ha—Whoo-ha,' made their way back to the tiny landing stage and their waiting passenger sampan poled by cheerful barefooted Chinese women.

Anne remained thoughtful during their journey. There was something rather odd about Emma's behaviour. Nothing she could point to—there was perhaps a slight puffiness to her features and her eyes seemed to hold a look of sly cunning as though she had discovered a secret to which she alone was privy. Then they boarded the ship and Anne shrugged off the thought as nothing other than fanciful imaginings. Emma had behaved with perfect propriety and her conversation with Dr McKrae had displayed no more than a natural curiosity as to the customs of an alien people.

She went below to her favourite room to discover the air stifling and the windows tightly closed, and learn that one of the customs about which she had been musing was to steal anything that wasn't nailed down.

The *Medusa*'s flooring chop of 450 chests and 230 half-chests was stowed in forty-eight hours, the coolie gangs working double shifts around the clock.

At 4 p.m. on the fifth day the cargo was topped off with 1,000 catty boxes and when the last box was loaded the *Medusa* was stowed with 1,234,406 lb of tea.

With the hatches at last battened down the crew set about their own work of preparing for the long voyage home. James was far from satisfied with the trim and had a dozen casks of salt provisions brought aft and lashed to the base of the mizzen mast and the holystones passed aft and stowed in the lazarette. Even then she rode three inches down by the head so he had forty chests and twenty half-chests of tea carried below and stowed in their staterooms.

By 4 a.m. they were ready, the *Medusa* drawing 18 ft. 5 in. aft and 18 ft. 1 in. forward.

At 5 a.m. the tug panted alongside and at 5.30 they hove up and proceeded down a river shrouded in early-morning mist. Once more the imperturbable Liu Hing was their pilot. 'Plenty water,' he smiled. 'Go chop-chop.'

James had sent one watch below; the job watch, with little to do until the tug cast off, slept sprawled on the main hatch.

The sun rose to tint the sky lemon and green and burn away the last swirls of mist and at 8.30 they dropped Liu Hing at Sharp Rock. James sent the hands to breakfast as their tug, *Island Queen*, took the strain of the tow rope and set off for the last haul to the Outer Knoll at the river mouth.

The tide was ebbing fast and bubbling over the shallows ahead. The tug, of low power and leaking pistons, hit the breakers and began to sheer and buck wildly. The tow-rope snapped, the tug lurched ahead and the *Medusa* began to swing toward a long sandbar already drying and gleaming in the sun as the river receded.

The carpenter and a couple of hands stationed on the fo'c's'le head and idly dreaming of home, suddenly came awake to their peril as James picked up the speaking trumpet. 'Let go! he bawled. The carpenter released the brake and the cable rattled out as the starboard anchor plunged to the river-bed.

The stern swung, touched the sandbank and then swung broadside on to be held fast, trapped between water and land as though in a vice.

The tug, hooting dementedly, came alongside and tried to haul them off until it, too, touched bottom. The tug's captain, a big, red-faced German, shrugged philosophically and signalled that they must wait for the next tide.

James muttered and cursed. Nor was his temper improved at the sight of the *Pandora*, towed by a larger, more powerful tug, gliding past. Daniel, standing on the poop deck, grinned, waved his hat and patted the barrel of his latest acquisition, a nine-pounder pop-gun mounted at the stern.

'A present from Emma,' he bawled and, grinning hugely, waved his hat in mock farewell.

With the jeers of her crew ringing in their ears they stood watching helplessly until the *Pandora* disappeared from view.

The Min River tides were of twelve hours' duration and they were forced to wait until 8.30 p.m. when the *Medusa* had enough water beneath her keel to be towed off.

Then the fates struck again. Quite suddenly the weather closed in, the wind blew from the north-east, rain fell in torrents, and the tug master refused to budge an inch until the weather cleared.

The *Pandora* now had a lead of fourteen hours, and increasing every minute as the *Medusa* remained stuck like a fly in treacle.

Two hours later the wind shifted, the rain stopped and the tug, straining every rivet, finally pulled the *Medusa* clear, then stood off as though proudly surveying its handiwork. James fumed and raged as the *Island Queen*'s lethargic crew slowly hauled in and coiled the stern hawser and equally slowly paid out the tow-rope.

At last they were able to heave up and,

choked and half-blinded by the clouds of filthy black smoke emitted by the *Island Queen*'s elongated smoke-stack, deafened by the clatter of her engines, they plodded in the tug's wake until, an hour and a half later, they crossed the bar and thankfully cast off the tow-rope.

Under a high yellow moon and a sky domed with stars, the *Medusa* filled her mainyard and stood away, south by east, for Turnabout Island, only to find Keay's *Falcon* and the *Ellen Rodger* hard on their heels.

There was a moderate north-east wind and all three ships set main skysails, fore topmast and lower stunsails at the same time.

Keay waved cheerfully, then the weather closed in again, rain tearing across the sea in wild gusts and blotting out all vision. By daybreak they had lost sight of each other and the *Medusa* stormed along alone beneath a wild sky from which hung curtains of rain and banks of smouldering cloud.

James settled himself for his long vigil on the quarterdeck. From this day forward he would rarely go below; no master of a racing clipper could relax until she was safely berthed in her home port; every inch of canvas counted, every yard, every sail must be trimmed just so; and of all water, the China Seas were the worst. Here there was no settled weather and every advantage had to be taken of the faintest ripple on the water. The wind could come howling from nowhere, die away to nothing, chop and change, bluster in squalls, cascade with rain. To add to a captain's difficulties, charts were hopelessly unreliable; reefs would appear where none had been noted; apparently clear channels would be strewn with rocks; entire islands would be charted five and six miles out of position; currents almost invariably behaved contrary to sailing directions.

And to add to their problems was the ever-present threat of pirates roving the seas in search of the rich pickings presented by a becalmed ship. They swept the waters from the Celebes to Cochin China and the combined strength of the navies of the world could not keep them at bay; for what one day would be a pirate lorcha would, the next, be an innocent fishing boat.

James had his canvas deck chair brought

out and a hammock slung; he took his meals on deck and bathed and shaved on deck; and reckoned on sleeping two out of twenty-four hours.

The *Medusa* followed the usual route south, down the China Seas, through the Formosa Channel to the Paracels; then she swung toward the Cochin China Coast.

James's log read: '5th Day. Light wind from S.E. 9 a.m. Pulo Canton in sight bearing W.½S., dist. 17 miles. Opened quarter hatch to ventilate hold. New topgallant mast sent up and coated with pine oil. Noon: lat: 15°18′N. long: 108°23′E. dist: 198 miles. Tacking as necessary. P.M. winds light. Watch variously employed about rigging. Midnight: fresh breeze from S.W. Tacked to S.S.E. Sighted coast of Cochin China about 6 miles distant. No sign of *Pandora*.'

And so it continued day after monotonous day.

On the twelfth day the airs were calm and baffling and a long patch of sea-fog rose like boiling steam to obscure their vision. Curling vapours hung over the sea in banks thirty feet high. Their topmasts were clear and sparkling in the sunlight, but on deck they could barely see a hand before their faces.

James calculated that they must be within the vicinity of the Prince of Wales Bank, a stretch of shoal water lying, if the chart were to be believed, at 9°55' North, 110°4' East. Mistrustful of the cartographer he sent leadsmen to the chains.

They were stealing through the fog when all hands heard the distinct bang of a gun coming from somewhere off the port bow.

James frowned, handed over the ship to Mr Armstrong, and scampered up the mizzen shrouds, as much glad of the exercise as of any serious consideration of a ship in difficulty, for it was by no means unknown for bored masters to occupy their time with a little gun practice.

He had always had a good head for heights and at the mizzen cross-trees, sixty feet above the deck, he settled himself comfortably, his back against the slightly swaying mast, and one hand gripping the topgallant rigging. The fog spread out before him and for a moment he had the pleasurable sensation of a wanderer in space flying above a sea of cloud. Overhead the sun blazed from a clear blue sky; below, as far as the eye could see, a white amorphous vapour wreathed and writhed, a slowly twisting blanket reaching to the far curves of the earth.

The bang was repeated and he imagined he caught the flash of a gun. Then the swirl of fog drifted and closed again, but not before he caught a distinct sight of the topmasts of a ship; and surrounding the ship the matted sails of a war junk accompanied by what he deduced to be a couple of lorchas.

He returned to deck and issued his orders quietly. Cutlasses and small arms were broken out and passed to the crew, Mr Llewellyn was sent below with instructions to rig the stern chasers, the two cannons were loaded and run out and absolute silence enjoined upon all hands. Then he took a moment to go below and reassure Anne.

He found her calmly packing away their breakables as Mr Llewellyn and four sweating seamen hauled in and set up the brass swivel guns.

'It seems that a British ship has run aground and is being attacked by a war junk and one or two lorchas,' he told her. 'I want you to take cover.' He pushed a chair behind a stack of tea chests as once again the flat report of the lone gun reverberated across the sea.

'Very well, James,' she said, placidly. 'But do persuade Mr Llewellyn to admit of as little damage as possible, this is such a beautiful room.'

'I shall send the carpenter and his mate to remove the windows,' he promised, kissed her lightly upon the forehead and returned to deck. She was a remarkable woman, he thought, a most remarkable woman.

The guns had been loaded and their crews were standing by while the rest of the hands were busily employed in tricing up the boarding nets, swayed out from the shipside and hanging loosely in order to afford poor handholds.

Again came the sharp bang of the gun, and James tried to starc through the swirling mist and identify the source of the sound. It was evidently a small gun, possibly from the British ship, but if so it was strange there was no answering fire from the heavy armament of the war junk. On the other hand the shots might be coming from one of the lorchas standing off and simply peppering the ship while the pirates and the crew fought it out hand to hand. If so all would be over in a few minutes.

He made up his mind, brought the *Medusa* round, and concentrated upon the immediate problem. The mist was both a blessing and a curse in that it successfully hid friend from foe until they were at close quarters, but also made navigation difficult. He had no wish to collide with one of the lorchas or, even worse, the junk; nor to run on a lee shore when they would be as helpless as the victim.

The wind seemed to puff and blow from every point of the compass; the sound of the gun became louder, closer; he imagined he heard shouts and yells. Then suddenly they broke through the fog into an uplift of air and a scene that etched sharply on his vision: The *Pandora* had run aground, bows on; clustered about her were four lorchas—odd-looking vessels, hybrids with Chinese rigs and westernised hulls of teak and camphor wood. Their screeching crews had succeeded in tearing holes in the protective boarding netting and were scrambling aboard and driving the desperate crew of the *Pandora* before them. One lorcha had evidently been holed by the *Pandora*'s nine-pounder and was slowly sinking, another had masts and sails cut to pieces, but the crews of the remainder were pouring over the side while the *Pandora*'s ratings hacked and slashed with cutlasses and boarding pikes.

James called down to Armstrong. 'Sink those lorchas, Mr Armstrong, then stand by to come about.'

The cannons roared spouting flame and smoke. One shot tore through the stern of the nearest lorcha, carried all before it and burst out through the bows. The second smashed into a tier of oarsmen desperately backing water to turn and meet the new threat. It struck the base of the mast, fragmented and spun through the deck in whistling fragments of iron.

Then the *Medusa* wore round and, presenting her stern to the mass of men scrambling up the *Pandora*'s side, brought her terrible stern chasers to bear. The sound was a muffled thump-thump, then a hail of small shot shrieked through the air to tear through flesh and bone and sweep the boarders into a screaming tangle of arms and legs.

James had time to see Daniel Fogarty, mouth open, teeth bared, roaring like a bull, swinging a cutlass in great scything chops, while around him men thrust and parried with knives, axes and mawls. A seaman, half-crazed with rage and fear, drove a boathook into the throat of an opponent and kept pushing until the man, with flailing arms, tumbled over the side and the hook tore out through jaw and cheek. The cook, brandishing a red-stained cleaver, cleared a path before him with murderous sweeps of his arm. Then James turned his head and realised why the war junk's guns had been so strangely silent.

She had also run aground, half a mile from the *Pandora* and out of range. A group of her seamen, shouting and screeching, were straining at the capstan bars in an effort to heave her off by means of a kedge anchor dropped over the stern. Others— and there seemed to be hundreds of them— were leaning over the side trying to fend her off with long bamboo poles.

The war junk was not unlike an old style galleon with a high after-castle and an overhanging lute-stern. She was about 150 feet long, flat-bottomed, and bore a forest of masts sticking out at ungainly angles. She also carried a formidable armament of ancient cannons, more than capable of blowing both the *Medusa* and the *Pandora* out of the water should she ever come to grips with them.

Even as he watched, the junk began to slowly slither and slide off the sandspit. With her crew cheering and capering, her clumsy slatted sails clattering and banging, she began to turn until the gaping muzzles of her enormous guns seemed to stare straight at them.

His stomach tightened and his mouth ran dry. 'Ready about!' he called. 'Helm a-lee. Up tacks and sheets. Mainsail haul!'

The *Medusa*'s sails shivered then filled as she spun on her heels and crossed the junk's vulnerable stern.

Mr Armstrong squinted along the barrel of the first cannon then, almost delicately, brought a glowing end of tarred hemp to the touch-hole.

The gun roared, gouted a sheet of flame, and a moment later the junk's flat stern burst open a little above the waterline. The shattered rudder hung loose, and the men struggling with the massive beam tiller were hurled into a tangled heap.

The second cannon banged and pieces flew from the extended lute-stern. A couple of iron cooking pots soared high in the air to fall with a splash a hundred feet away.

The *Medusa* came about again, brought her sternchasers to bear and poured a storm of flailing metal into the junk's after-castle before disappearing into the bank of fog.

James waited until the cannons were reloaded and run out and then prepared to take the *Medusa* back. Their only hope of success was to attempt to cross and re-cross the junk's stern and pound away until she sank. A series of heavy explosions followed by the throbbing whistle of round shot showed that the junk's gunners were firing blindly at their tormentor. The *Medusa* began to creep ahead again while James tried to hold a mental picture of the junk's last position. Then suddenly the fog seemed to bloom with red and orange light, and a thunderclap of sound erupted to stun their senses. The sky rained splinters of timber, blocks and pulleys, fragments of copper and lumps of iron. A length of broken deck planking spun end over end to tear the *Medusa*'s mainsail to tatters, and one of the seamen standing by the lee rail suddenly let out a howl—as much of surprise as pain—as a shard of bamboo speared him by the shoulder.

Then suddenly they were out of the fog and into bright sunlight.

The junk had disappeared, its place being taken by a sea of tossing wreckage and a score or so of broken bodies. Pieces of masts and parts of slatted bamboo sails floated aimlessly among the flotsam and a surf already staining red.

They never discovered the cause. Possibly embers from the cooking fires had been blown into the powder magazine by the *Medusa*'s second shot; possibly it was simply the result of carelessness—pirates not being notably self-disciplined. Whatever the cause the result was the same: the battle was over.

The wind shifted to blow sharply from the north-east and whisk the fog into scattered puffballs that rolled and danced away over the sea. The *Pandora*'s sails backed and filled and she slowly wriggled herself free of the grip of sand and coral.

James stood off until he was sure the *Pandora* was undamaged, then he raised a hand in farewell to Fogarty, brought the *Medusa* round on a south-west heading and set a course for the Sunda Straits and the Indian Ocean.

There was still a race to be won.

CHAPTER 17

JAMES'S log read:

'21st Day: 1 a.m. Approaching Cape St Nicholas, 10 miles bearing south. Current setting 1½ knots to N.N.W.
3.30 a.m. Set staysails and foretopmast and topgallant stunsails and Jamie Green. Yards sharp up, wind freeing.
7 a.m. Off Anjer. Hoisted our number. Took on fowls, fresh water. Posted letters for Albert, Robert and Tupman. Postage one dollar each.
Noon lat. 6°8'S., long. 106°36'E. All possible sail set.
11 p.m. Entered Strait. Many vessels bound north. No sign of *Pandora*.

'22nd Day: 2.30 a.m. Cleared Krakatao Island and entered Indian Ocean. Fine steady moderate breeze from E.S.E.
Noon lat. 7°50'S., long. 103°11'E.
Pandora well astern, leaving Strait under full spread of canvas. Spied through telescope. Vessel seems none the worse

for wear after brush with pirates.

'23rd Day: Noon lat. 10°5′S., long. 100°16′E. Distance 280 miles.
P.M. Hands employed holystoning decks ready for varnishing tomorrow.
Pandora bearing south about 6 miles but not closed distance.'

They picked up the Trades and the *Medusa* stretched her legs and flew over the sea. She carried every stitch of canvas she could bear from jib-o'-jib to ring-tail, her decks were awash and every line hummed and sang. Day after day they reeled off the knots and in a week she had run 2,000 miles. But still they could not shake off the *Pandora*. Hull down on the horizon she matched the *Medusa* sail for sail, knot for knot.

Anne spent less and less time on deck, and on the few occasions she did venture from the seclusion of her cabin tended to lean more and more heavily upon her walking stick. She had given up her little promenades and now simply sat in a canvas chair dozing and dreaming under the benison of the hot sun until a warning twist of pain would send her limping below again.

Each day she found it increasingly necessary to take a draught of Dr McKrae's Chinese medicine. It was by no means unpleasant, and had a rather soporific effect, as well as deadening the pain. Before leaving Foochow he had called once again and left half a dozen bottles with particular instructions as to their use. She was grateful to him; he had proved to be a kindly man, his troubled face showing concern at her condition, and she was sure that he had impressed James with the urgency of the matter.

Lying on the settee by the open stern windows she smiled at the thought. As though James needed urging! He was driving the ship like a demon, only coming below for a few minutes at a time to sit beside her, hold her hand and inquire anxiously if she was all right. Understanding his need for reassurance she would agree gravely that she had never felt better and that occasional twinges and spasms were only to be expected under the circumstances. Then he would crack his knuckles, rub his hands together and count off the days.

Twelve days out from Anjer they passed Mauritius.

'We are making three hundred and forty miles a day,' he told her. 'Only another fortnight and we shall round the Cape and enter the Atlantic. Then one long haul and we'll be home.'

He made it sound as though they were almost within sight of New Brighton pier, but in fact, given good weather all the way, there were another sixty-five days to go. She, too, had been computing with an unease she did not care to admit even to herself, but she nodded as though completely satisfied, told him not to concern himself and that she had every confidence they would arrive with ample time to spare.

After he left she made herself as comfortable as her circumstances would allow and bent industriously to the task of crocheting a bonnet for the baby.

Buried beneath towers of canvas the *Pandora* tore along like a wild thing in the wake of her rival. In addition to her full suit of racing canvas she carried ring-tails and save-alls, and was winged with spare mizzen staysails laced to the lower stunsails; a bonnet was laced on the foresail, watersails hauled out beneath passaree booms, and a jib topsail run up the fore royal stay. She kept the *Medusa* in sight but seemed unable to close the gap. At night the two ships would lose sight of each other, but with the coming of dawn the other's white sails would just be visible above the horizon.

There was no doubt in Daniel's mind that he was in for the race of his life. The *Medusa* was a flyer. Day after day, eyes red-rimmed and smarting from lack of sleep, he kept his gaze fixed upon that tantalising patch of whiteness etched against the blue sky. Never once did their relative positions alter by so much as a yard. 'Being towed by the wake,' in the parlance of the fo'c's'le hands; and some were even superstitious enough to believe it, claiming it brought bad luck to sever this invisible umbilical cord.

He saw little of Emma. Occasionally she would join him on deck; usually to do no more than loll and doze in a hammock.

Once or twice he caught her nodding and smiling knowingly to herself, and he began to fear for her reason, wondering if perhaps the shock of their bloody encounter with the pirates had unhinged her mind. Her behaviour had been odd, almost as though part of her had taken to living in a secret world of its own. He tried, whenever the demands of the ship would permit, to share at least one meal a day with her when she would eat delicately, always smiling that strange inner secretive smile. Sometimes she would run her fingers through his hair, complain that his horrid ship was keeping him away from her. 'Don't you want to bed me, Daniel?' she would ask, and he was never wholly sure whether she was mocking or enticing him.

Prowling fore and aft along the weather-side of the poop, with the Southern Cross slowly wheeling in the sky, he puzzled and brooded, unable to arrive at a conclusion. She needed a firm hand. That had been Callon's advice and, as her father, who should know better? But it was like trying to grasp a will-o'-the-wisp. Sometimes she would be pliant and obedient, at others rage like a spitfire. At least their bouts of love-making had become more frequent, she submitting with goodwill rather than wifely complicity, but certainly no longer showing the marked repugnance she had hitherto exhibited. Her eyes would remain open and vague and her voice cool and remote. When she murmured, 'Yes, wife me, Daniel, wife me,' it sounded like another person. And her behaviour was becoming more childlike; she would sleep late, nap in the afternoon, and stuff herself from a private hoard of sweetmeats purchased in Foochow. She had taken to whispering and muttering to herself when she thought herself alone, and now and again he caught her examining him with a look of sly cunning.

As the dawn rose astern to wash the sky a flamingo-pink he abandoned the unprofitable train of thought and concentrated his full attention upon searching the far horizon for sight of those elusive top-masts.

As yet, to the west, sky and water met in a fusion of inky blackness, but even as he watched the sea began to ripple with colour as the sun lifted to shower the world with gold.

Something glittered and sparkled, and the *Medusa*'s topsails suddenly stood out clear white against the black background of night. Daniel put the telescope to his eye and counted: royals, t'gallants, upper and lower topsails. He caught his breath and slapped the telescope shut. Upper and lower topsails! For days they had barely glimpsed her royals and t'gallants! At last the *Pandora* was closing the gap!

He schooled himself to wait an hour and then looked again. Held in the ring of the telescope's eye there was no mistaking: the *Medusa* was clearly outlined, hull down against the horizon.

Containing his exultation he forced himself to think: Why should a ship of the *Medusa*'s pace suddenly become a laggard? The answer must be the wind. The wind ahead had fallen away. Daniel chewed his lip. If they continued on their present course then inevitably they, too, would enter that same area of light airs and their gains be lost.

The sea around had the look of polished glass. He clambered up the mizzen rigging and, squinting against the glare of reflected light, scanned the horizon. Far to the south he thought he saw a faint dark riffling of water.

He made his decision quickly, wore round and bore away to the south'ard.

A little after noon they overtook the *Medusa* and triumphantly left her sluggishly flapping her wings away to the north.

James entered in his log:

'Day 38: Barometer 30.60. Light airs. Carpenter fitting fore-topmast yardarm iron. Watch employed in greasing masts, cleaning brass-work, oiling yard trusses, etc.

Noon lat. 32°30′S., long. 34°45′E. Distance 240 miles. *Pandora* bore away to south, fetched wind, overtook us. Weather clear.'

It was a laconic entry masking his frustration at the contrariness of the weather. Not that he was particularly disturbed by the change of lead, but rather that he was becoming increasingly concerned over Anne's condition.

Her face was becoming pinched with pain and she walked with the greatest difficulty. But when he had suggested putting into Table Bay where she could receive the best of medical attention, she had shaken her head obstinately and sworn their son would be born in Liverpool or not at all. He had eyed her swollen figure with misgivings but, hopelessly ignorant of the mysteries of child-bearing, had given way.

'The weather will not hold fair for ever,' he had warned her. 'We might be in for quite a tossing rounding the Cape.'

She had considered calmly for a few moments, then suggested that the carpenter might fit a padded rail to the side of the settee; and there, supported by a barricade of cushions, she lay day-long, gazing out at the panorama of the sea, her fingers busy sewing, stitching, hemming, until the night closed in and she rested, with the swinging oil lamps throwing golden orbs of light about the room.

The *Pandora* had increased her lead to four miles and the two ships weathered the Cape together with a gale of wind roaring from the south-east. Leaping and plunging, smothered in water, a vicious cross sea from the Aghula Current making them almost unmanageable, they clawed their way round and out into the Atlantic. Then they hauled to the north. James, breaking out t'gallants and royals, took the inshore passage and brought the *Pandora* abeam.

They sailed neck and neck, two leaning pyramids of canvas, and eleven days later brought up St Helena. Four more days of straining every tack and sheet brought the lonely outpost of Ascension Island in sight.

Then, two degrees south of the line, sweeping belts of rain and variable winds warned that they were entering the Doldrums.

They found the *Falcon* and the *Ellen Rodger* lying with limp sails and their heads pointing all around the compass. For a few minutes the *Medusa* and *Pandora* ghosted along then their sails shivered and folded and they, too, lay becalmed.

The Doldrums was the meeting place of the N.E. and S.E. Trades; a wide, shifting band of low pressure producing calms and sudden strong upward movements of air. A region of heavy rains, thunderstorms, and squalls that came from nowhere. An area in which ships could be becalmed for hours, or for days; dreaded by sailing-ship men the world over; but it gave James the opportunity he had been seeking to try out a new sail plan. The two ships were obviously evenly matched, but if one could be rigged so that it gained but a yard or two an hour over the other, the race—barring accidents—would be won.

Praying that the calm would last, he called out all hands and set to work. They took off the main yards and re-rigged them on the foremast, then new yards, fashioned by the carpenter and six feet longer than the old, were replaced on the mainmast. The *Medusa* could now carry two extra widths of canvas on the fore and three on the main.

By midnight they had completed the work. James kept four men on watch, sent the rest below, handed over the ship to Mr Armstrong with instructions to call him at the first puff of breeze, then took himself below.

He had intended to keep Anne company for an hour or two, but had hardly spoken a dozen words when he sank into a sound sleep in the unaccustomed comfort of a plush-upholstered cabin chair.

Anne smiled as his snores reverberated around the room. Then she touched her stomach as the child kicked and kicked again.

Emma awoke to the crash of thunder and the flare of lightning. She blinked open her eyes to drag herself from the depths of a dream in which she was a silk-clad concubine in a marble palace heaped with treasure. There had been golden pomegranates hanging from silver trees, chattering Barbary apes with jewelled eyes, and a tall richly robed wizard holding out taloned hands. It had been a pleasant dream, almost exactly duplicating Dr McKrae's description of a mandarin's palace.

The room lit once again with an unearthly glare and the following peal of thunder seemed to split the sky. She was not in the least alarmed, for the wine and the sweetmeats had given her power over fear.

It was in Hong Kong that she had first become aware of the potency of the distillations prepared by the Chinese necromancers. They had the power of removing one's wits and replacing them with an altogether delightful sense of well-being; loosening the tongue and painting images of quite extraordinary intensity across the mind's eye. In Foochow she had ordered a great quantity of rice wine and smuggled it aboard in lacquered chests which she kept locked in her private room. Taken in moderation it had a wondrous effect, both soothing and enlightening, occasionally stimulating and always, of course, protecting. For had not Dr McKrae described in the minutest detail the manners and customs of this mysterious race of sorcerers? He had shown her paintings of venerable sages with incantations of blood-red characters pouring from their lips, and she had recognised them immediately as pictures of wizards from her childhood story books. Therefore it was only to be expected that in a country riddled with superstition and ruled by wizards, love-potions and spell-casting would be a common practice. The only problem had been to discover which were the beneficial and which the malevolent nostrums; this she had resolved when Dr McKrae had described some of the delicacies especially prepared for a mandarin's concubinage. Obviously nothing swallowed by those bird-like creatures could be anything but beneficial.

She had quite quickly learned the secret: the wine gave power, the confections stimulated the appetites. Naturally she had hidden the wine from Daniel, knowing that should the secret of her power ever be divulged, the spell would be broken.

So she would sip a couple of small cups upon rising in the morning, a couple more after lunch, and perhaps two or three before retiring. Not a great deal it would seem, but her store of bottles was certainly diminishing, and she had begun to wonder how she could possibly replace them when they returned to England.

The lightning flashed again and again in blue and yellow sheets, and the room seemed filled with the noise of thunder. She felt a stir of movement in the bed and realised for the first time that Daniel must have quietly slipped in beside her. He was sleeping the sleep of total exhaustion and for a moment she was tempted to wake him, to once again impose the power given by the magic wine. She listened for the wine-voice to tell her what to do, half-hoping it would instruct her—as it had so often done in the past—to treat him cruelly; tempt and torment him then, as his ardour increased, push him away and spurn his attentions. That delighted her more than anything else. Even though he darkened with anger she knew he was quite helpless against her power. Sometimes, as a reward, she would permit him to roll on top of her, submitting to the pushings and heavings she once found so repulsive with bland acceptance; even to the extent of occasionally uttering murmurs of encouragement taught her by Precious Emma, her shadow-companion who now accompanied her everywhere, and with whom she often held long private conversations.

She listened again. 'Repose,' the wine-voice told her. 'Repose.' Contentedly she closed her eyes and, while Daniel twitched in his sleep, returned to her dream-world far, far from the wilderness of the sea.

By dawn the storm had tumbled away to the south to flicker and flare across the horizon. James yawned and stretched then, leaving Anne asleep, washed and changed and made his way on to deck to find the sea flat and calm beneath the oven-heat of the sun. The cook was rattling his pots and pans in the galley and the other ships were beginning to stir into life. Mr Armstrong had been relieved by Mr Llewellyn who, glancing up at the limp sails, greeted James with an apologetic shrug of the shoulders as though expecting to bear responsibility for the lack of wind.

James, about to bid him good morning, cocked his head and listened instead. He listened again, turned his head and, half-perplexed, counted the ships scattered about the ocean. Where there should have been three others rising and falling, slowly pirouetting in the pull of the western-flowing current, there were now four. The newcomer was a deep-laden four-masted barque. What was more it was under way; he could clearly see her bow wave and the change in her silhouette. And yet there was not a breath of wind.

'Cook, there!' he rasped. 'Belay that noise, damn you!'

The sounds from the galley ceased and the cook's woolly black head poked out inquiringly.

The watch, turning-to for their morning task of washing down the decks, also stopped in their tracks and listened.

The windjammer came steadily on, puffing and panting, wheezing and gasping, a plume of dark smoke rising from a stubby

369

funnel poking up from the after deck. She evidently had a small auxiliary engine for just such an emergency and chugged steadily through the becalmed tea fleet until the soft slow chunk of her propeller died away and she plodded on to disappear beyond the northern horizon.

'The tortoise and the hares, by damn,' said Llewellyn. 'There is truth in that fable, I am thinking.'

'As you have such a fondness for old wives' tales, you might try whistling up a wind,' said James sourly, and took himself off to his privileged weather side.

The crestfallen Mr Llewellyn possibly had whistled beneath his breath, for an hour later a light north-east Trade sprang up and the four ships stood away with every rag that would draw hung out.

For two days the Trade remained light and steady. The *Falcon* and *Ellen Rodger* drew away to the west as the *Medusa* and *Pandora* continued to run beam and beam. Then the wind began to freshen and on the third day they overtook the windjammer, all sails set and labouring along at a steady nine knots.

Eight days from the equator they cleared

the Cape Verdes with the *Medusa*'s new sail plan just edging her into the lead. Seventeen days later they sighted the *Falcon* and *Ellen Rodger* again and as they neared Flores in the Western Isles all four ships began to close up with a fresh south-west wind driving them forward in furies of foam.

With the *Medusa* leading the pack they sighted Bishop Rock lighthouse on the sixth day and parted company, the *Falcon* and *Ellen Rodger* tearing up-Channel under royals, stunsails and flying kites, while the *Medusa* and *Pandora* stretched for the north and the St George's Channel.

As the ships bore away from each other, Keay waved to James and threw his hat in the air in gesture of defeat and James grinned acknowledgement before returning his full attention to the last lap.

The *Pandora*, sails almost bursting under the pressure, hung on to the *Medusa*'s skirts. In twenty-five hours of furious sailing they passed the South Stack and sighted the Skerries ahead.

James, hoping to shake off the *Pandora*, took the *Medusa* inside the Skerries with a south-west wind churning the sea into a seething race of water and bringing clouds of driving rain to blot out the land. The *Pandora* doggedly followed, thrusting aside the sea and driving through the narrow, rock-strewn channel in a welter of spume and a smother of water.

Six miles from Point Lynas, with both ships flying their numbers, the *Medusa*'s main course suddenly exploded into a thing of shreds and tatters, the weather brace parted and the massive new yard swung wildly to cockbill and crash into the lower topsail yard. The *Medusa* yawed and lost way, sails shaking and thundering. Then the main royal blew out.

The watch below tumbled out on to deck and, some in shirt tails, joined the scramble aloft while the *Pandora*, beating to windward, snored triumphantly past, heading for the distant pilot cutter battling into the teeth of the gale.

Anne whimpered as the pains came again. Hair dank, face bathed in perspiration, she gritted her teeth and tried to prevent herself from crying out. Her eyes rolled in their sockets, searching the room for help that could not come.

'Oh, God!' she moaned. 'Oh, God, oh,

God, oh, God . . .!' Then suddenly James's concerned face loomed into the periphery of her vision.

He put a hand to her forehead. 'What is it?' he asked anxiously.

'Oh, dear God, James . . . I'm sorry. Sorry . . . the pains . . . the pains have started . . . Oh, dear God . . .'

He gulped, more afraid than she. 'The child . . .?'

'I think . . . I think so . . . Oh, God, yes. I'm sorry, James. I'm sorry . . .' She began to weep and jerk convulsively.

'I'll do everything possible,' said James, beside himself with panic. 'But you must tell me. I don't know.'

'Not yet,' she said. 'Not yet. There is a little time.'

He hopped from one foot to the other. 'Wait,' he told her idiotically, praying don't please God have the child yet, not yet; then ran from the room and out on to deck.

Llewellyn had led the way out on the mainyard and was reaving a new brace, while Armstrong ran up the ship's numbers and screamed hoarsely at the crew to prepare to heave to, and the hands rushed to back the head yards.

James looked across to the *Pandora* lying-to with her yards counterbraced, pitching and rolling easily as she waited for the pilot cutter to come alongside under her lee.

'Belay that order, Mr Armstrong,' said James, curtly.

Armstrong gestured weakly. 'The pilot, sir?'

'Keep her as she goes,' snapped James.

The *Medusa* stormed past the *Pandora*, unheeding of shouts from the pilot cutter, a flurry of flags from the signal station and a bellow of rage from Fogarty. James gave clear and unequivocal instructions to Armstrong and then hurried below to Anne.

With a frenzy of flags streaming from her signal halyards the *Medusa* flew upriver to be met by a snorting Frazer tug, while the *Pandora*, having made up lost ground and now trailing only ten minutes astern, picked up her tug only to find the lock gates closed in her face.

An ambulance waited at the quayside, its pair of horses snickering and champing at their bits as Anne, only half-conscious, gasping and moaning in anguish, was carried gently from the ship and lifted from the stretcher to the cot inside.

Albert stood beside the open doors. 'Everything is arranged,' he told James. 'She will be driven to your house where two of the best medical men in Liverpool are waiting.'

James only half-heard, as he stepped into the ambulance and seated himself beside Anne. She opened her eyes as he tenderly wiped the perspiration from her face. She managed to drag her features into the semblance of a smile.

'Off with you, James,' she said. 'You attend to your business, while I attend to mine.'

'I'm coming with you,' he stated, flatly.

'No, sir, you are not,' announced a firm voice, and a stern-visaged lady in the uniform of a Nightingale nurse bulked against the light. 'I can only deal with one patient at a time. Outside, if you please.'

'Anne . . .' he said, lowered his head and kissed her gently.

She clutched his hand for a moment and smiled up at him. 'It will be all right,' she whispered. 'It will be all right. I promise.'

He lingered for a moment and then, as her eyes closed, allowed himself to be led unresistingly away.

The door closed, the bell clanged and the ambulance rolled away on its silent rubber-shod tyres. He waited until it had disappeared from view, then Albert touched his arm.

'Come along. My carriage is waiting. Where do you wish to go?'

James tried to clear his head of a fog which seemed to cloud his brain.

'Mitchell's office,' he said, at length.

'At least, you won the race,' said Albert, as they settled themselves in the closed brougham.

'I think not,' said James, bleakly. 'I threw it away.' And as they bowled along toward South Castle Street he outlined the events leading to his decision to ignore the pilot.

Albert brooded for a while then lifted his shoulders in a shrug of acceptance. 'You'll be disqualified, of course. But it can't be helped—you had no choice.' He grinned at James. 'We'll just have to build another ship.'

James, his mind far away, grunted. 'Is it completed?'

'Ready for launching,' said Albert. 'We were going to call her the *Anne Onedin*. Elizabeth had been elected to christen her in spite of Robert's claims for the honour. Robert has moved up in the world during your absence. Member of the Chamber of Commerce, prospective candidate for the Council—in the Liberal interest, of course. I'll say one thing for Robert—he invariably knows upon which side his bread is buttered. I have also resolved that other problem,' he added, chattily, in a transparent effort to keep James's mind fully occupied.

'What problem?' asked James, with total lack of interest.

'The steering engine. I was racking my brains, and one day I had the misfortune to be overturned in a hansom.' He looked away and coughed delicately as though something in the memory embarrassed him. 'I noticed one wheel spinning on its axis—and there was the solution! Nothing more simple! Put the hub of a wheel over the rudder head, fit the rim with cogs, gear the cogs to a worm wheel. Two sets of pistons drive the worm and turn the rudder from side to side. Simple.' Privately, Albert thought it a stroke of genius.

'Good, good, glad to hear it,' said James absently, as the carriage drew up outside Mitchell's office.

'I'll wait,' announced Albert, philosophically aware that a prophet was traditionally without honour in his own country.

James left Albert to his ruminations and pushed open the door of Mitchell's office.

Daniel Fogarty was already there, hands behind his back and pacing up and down like a caged lion, while Mitchell, as bland as ever, sat contentedly sipping sherry wine.

'Ah, there you are!' snarled Daniel. 'You could have saved yourself the trouble of the visit. I claim the race by default!'

Mitchell stroked a match down the side of a silver box and enticed the flame to the end of a cigar.

'Am I to understand, Mr Onedin, that you docked without waiting for a pilot?'

'I did,' James replied, curtly. 'My wife was nearing her time.'

'Mm.' Mitchell exhaled thin spirals of

smoke. 'So you were prepared to abandon a race almost won?'

'Almost won! I had taken the lead! The race was in my pocket until Onedin stooped to his usual sharp practice. I'd have outsailed him up the river. I could outsail him anywhere!' Daniel's face was flushed with anger.

'You couldn't outsail a herring boat,' James told him, coldly. He turned to Mitchell. 'The agreement reads: "The first ship to put a line ashore". There is nothing in it concerning pilotage.'

'It is implicit that we were to comply with harbour regulations,' retorted Daniel. He appealed to Mitchell. 'It is like cheating at cards.'

Mitchell drew on his cigar, drummed pudgy fingers upon the table, and considered for long moments while a fly buzzed and blundered about the room and Daniel glowered his anger at James.

'If,' Mitchell pronounced, eventually, 'Mr Onedin chooses to invoke the wrath of the harbour authorities—whatever his motives—that is his affair. I am a sporting man, gentlemen, and admire a man prepared to put all to the hazard. Mr

Onedin's was undoubtedly the first ship to dock, and therefore must be declared the winner.' He took a portfolio of documents from the desk drawer and tossed it upon the table. 'My congratulations, sir.'

CHAPTER 18

WEBSTER clung to Anne's hand and refused to leave.

Anne, breathing laboriously, opened her eyes. 'You must go now, Father,' she told him. 'Go now. It will soon be over.'

The old lined face crumpled, and the pale watery eyes that had witnessed so much brimmed with tears. Slowly he relinquished his hold and allowed the nurse to guide him to the door.

As the door closed behind him, Anne's body arched and twisted. 'Oh, quickly,' she begged. 'Oh, quickly, please!'

The two doctors, sleeves rolled up, rubber aprons about their waists, emerged from behind a tall screen set across a corner of the room. The taller of the two, of freckled arms and beard peppered with grey, spoke softly to her.

'I can promise but one thing, Mrs Onedin. It will be entirely painless.'

Behind her head the nurse prepared a gauze mask and held it over Anne's mouth and nose. A sweet, ethereal odour began to fill the room as the second doctor began to drip chloroform upon the gauze.

Anne began to retch and choke, tried to pluck away the mask.

The nurse held the mask more firmly.

'Inhale deeply. Try to relax,' instructed the doctor.

'James . . .' said Anne. 'James . . .' Then her struggles ceased and she relaxed into the long sighing breaths of deep sleep.

The nurse pulled back the bed covers as the tall surgeon pushed away the folding screen and, at a nod from his colleague, picked up a scalpel.

James arrived to find an anxious, silent group congregated in the hall. Old Webster, seated on a hard-back chair, stared into his memories. A solemn Robert. Sarah biting at a handkerchief. Elizabeth looking pale and frightened as she moved across to join Albert, entering on James's heels. A lugubrious Baines, rubbing his big hands together as though washing away sins of omission.

'Not yet,' said Elizabeth in answer to James's unspoken question. 'Not yet.'

He could not remain still, but with the habit of a lifetime took to pacing slowly up and down, restless with unease, his mind numb with panic. He glanced up once to find Baines at his shoulder.

'I'm sorry,' mumbled the giant. 'Truly sorry.'

'What—?' James blinked dazedly at the dolt. What was he trying to say?

'The *Pampero*,' said Baines. 'She went down off the Horn.'

'Oh?' It took James an interminable time to digest the information. Then he waved a hand. 'It is of no consequence,' he said. 'She was insured.'

'Is that all ye can put your mind to at a time like this?' rumbled the old man. 'Money! D'ye concern yourself with nothing but money?'

James shook his head as though ridding himself of a bothersome fly, and resumed his silent pacing.

The grandfather clock slowly tocked seconds into minutes, then suddenly their heads jerked up to the unmistakable squawl of a new-born infant.

The breath left their bodies in a combined whooosh of relief, and Albert clapped James upon the shoulder. 'Con-gratulations,' he beamed. 'You are a father!'

Robert mopped his brow. 'By heaven, I wouldn't go through that again for a thousand pounds!' He blew through his whiskers and pumped James by the hand. 'Next time, brother, do not cut it so fine!'

Then they were crowding around him, laughing, shaking hands, crowing with delight. Elizabeth hugged and kissed him. 'Don't look so dismal, you greaty booby. You are a father. Do you understand—a father!'

'Join the club,' grinned Albert, winking broadly.

James shook them off and moved towards the stairs, to find Sarah barring his way.

'You can't go in yet,' she said. 'There are—' She waved her arms. 'Things to be done. Anne must be prepared.'

James ran a hand through his hair. 'Ah, yes,' he said, distraught. 'Yes, yes, of course, of course. We must wait,' he explained to them, carefully. 'Wait. And keep calm.'

They waited, chattering imbecilely, until the clock struck three savage hours. Then the door opened and the nurse stood upon the threshold.

'Mr Onedin,' she called down quietly. 'You may come up now.'

They followed him as he took the stairs three at a time. At the bedroom door the nurse allowed James to enter and firmly kept the others back. There was something about the set of her features that silenced their voices.

'She's my daughter,' said Webster, and pushed his way inside.

Anne lay still and quiet, eyes closed, face still and calm in the eternal repose of death. James stood beside her, his features stiff and frozen, drained of emotion.

'I'm sorry,' said the surgeon. 'We did all we could.'

The nurse entered and picked up a wriggling, red-faced, bawling bundle. 'You have a daughter, Mr Onedin. Would you like to hold her?'

James stared blankly, then turning on his heel, walked away.

Webster held out his arms and cradled the child. He rocked it to-and-fro in time with his body. 'My little Anne,' he crooned. 'My poor little Anne.'

Without any sense of direction, his mind empty of all but the pain of inconsolable loss, James made his way down to the docks. He walked for miles; past sailing ships and steamers, deep-sea traders and coasters, ships discharging cargoes from every corner of the earth, ships loading the produce of industry—coal and iron; machinery; cotton and linen goods; salt; glassware; foundryware; furniture and upholstery; zinc; pig lead; firearms—there seemed no end to the outpourings of the manufactories.

Across the river, furnace fires flared and roared, burning the pale wash of the evening sky into a deeper, fiercer glow. Smoke poured from tall factory chimneys to eddy and wave in dark clouds above the city. He could hear the incessant ringing of hammers as though Liverpool herself were the anvil of the world.

Unaccountably he found himself at Frazer's yards, looking up at the monstrous bulk of Albert's dream. The ship stood stark and bare, silent and alone at the head of the slipway. Plated sides, studded with rivets, lent her the appearance of a sleeping dragon. The bows rose to curve and flare high above his head and the stem curved away to meet the keel far below. She was a concept of the age, a thing of raw, brutal power.

James turned his back upon the ship and stared for a long while out across the river, to homeward-bounders and outward-bounders, piled with canvas, to ferry boats scuttling across like insects, up to the skies and the high wild call of the endlessly circling gulls.

He made up his mind: The world had taken her from him; the world should be made to pay.

THE END

The story of the Onedin Line will be continued in another volume.

FICTION TITLES IN THE ULVERSCROFT LARGE PRINT SERIES

We hope this Large Print edition gives you the pleasure and enjoyment we ourselves experienced in its publication.

There are now 1,000 titles available in this ULVERSCROFT Large Print Series. Ask to see a Selection at your nearest library.

The Publisher will be delighted to send you, free of charge, upon request a complete and up-to-date list of all titles available.

Ulverscroft Large Print Books Ltd.
The Green, Bradgate Road
Anstey, Leicester
England

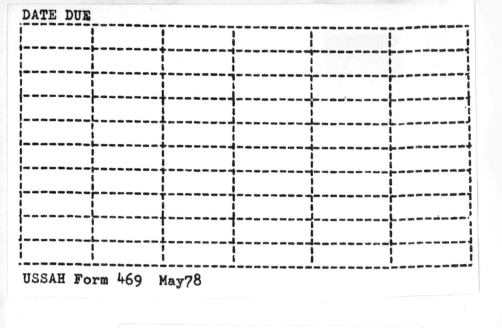
842166